Letts

EDUCATIONAL

ADVANCED
SUBSIDIARY

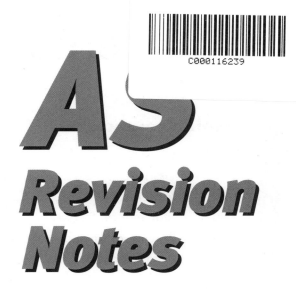

AS
Revision
Notes

Biology

Author
John Parker

Contents

The genetic code

Continuity of life

Energy and ecosystems

Human health and disease

Progress check answers

Index

Biological molecules

Carbohydrates

Monosaccharides

- Carbohydrates consist of carbon (C), hydrogen (H) and oxygen (O).
- The formula of a carbohydrate is always $C_x(H_2O)_n$.
- Where n = 6 the molecular formula is $C_6H_{12}O_6$. This is the formula shared by glucose and other **monosaccharides** like fructose.
- $C_6H_{12}O_6$ does not indicate how the atoms bond together. A number of –H and –OH groups are bonded to the carbon atom 'skeleton' of the molecule. The different positions of these groups on the carbon chain are responsible for different properties of the molecules.
- Molecules which have the same molecular formula but different structural formulae are known as **isomers**.
- The structural formulae of the isomers, α and β glucose are shown below.

The carbon atoms in each monosaccharide ring can be numbered

Disaccharides

- Each glucose unit is known as a **monomer** and is capable of linking others.
- When two monosaccharide monomers bond together a **disaccharide** is formed.
- The diagram shows two molecules of α glucose forming the disaccharide, maltose.

A **condensation** reaction means that as two molecules bond together a water molecule is produced. The link formed between the two glucose molecules is known as a **glycosidic bond**. The maltose molecule above has a 1-4 glycoside bond.

Polysaccharides

- They consist of many monomer units linked by glycosidic bonds.
- Chains of these 'sugar' units are known as **polymers**. These larger molecules have important structural and storage roles.
- Starch consists of two polysaccharides, amylose and amylopectin.

Amylose is

- an unbranched chain of 200–1500 glucose units
- linked by 1-4 glycosidic bonds

Amylopectin

- consists of branched chains of over 2000 glucose units
- has branch junctions joined by 1-6 glycosidic bonds

This is a 1-6 glycoside bond. The numbers of the carbon atoms in each 'monosaccharide' ring are not always given. You can remember them!

- Cellulose is a chain of 2000–3000 glucose units.

carbohydrate		
monosaccharide	**disaccharide**	**polysaccharide**
glucose	maltose	starch
fructose	sucrose	glycogen
galactose	lactose	cellulose & pectins

Carbohydrate digestion

- Glycosidic bonds can be broken down to release separate monomer units.
- A water molecule is needed to break each glycosidic bond.
- This is **hydrolysis** because water is needed to split up the bigger molecules.

Examiner's Tip

During the formation of a glycosidic bond a water molecule is given off (**condensation**). During the breaking of a glycosidic bond a water molecule is needed (**hydrolysis**). All of the digestive enzymes are hydrolytic!

- They are fats, oils and waxes which consist of the elements carbon, hydrogen and oxygen.
- There is always a high proportion of carbon and hydrogen, with a small proportion of oxygen.
- The essential bond is the ester bond.

The diagram shows the structural formula of a typical fat.

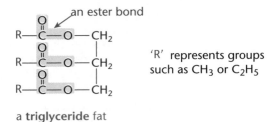

'R' represents groups such as CH_3 or C_2H_5

a **triglyceride** fat

How are fats formed?

- Fatty acids react with glycerol.
- Water is produced during triglyceride formation (condensation reaction).
- Different triglyceride fats are formed using different fatty acids.

3 fatty acids   glycerol   a triglyceride fat   water

How are fats broken down?

- The reaction is the reverse of the one shown above.
- A triglyceride fat can be broken down into glycerol and fatty acids by the enzyme **lipase** (lipase is a hydrolysing enzyme!).

a triglyceride fat   water   3 fatty acids   glycerol

How useful are lipids?

- Used to make **phospholipid** molecules, a major part of the cell surface membrane.
- Used as high **energy** supply.
- Excellent storage qualities due to their **insolubility** in water and **compact** structure.
- Thermal **insulator** in adipose cells.
- **Electrical insulator** around nerve axons.
- **Mechanical** support around our soft organs.

Phospholipid structure

A triglyceride fat can be converted into a **phospholipid**. Phosphoric acid replaces one of the fatty acids of a triglyceride. (Phospholipids are important components of cell surface membranes! See page 30)

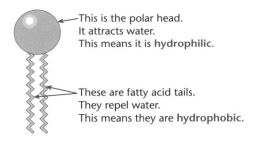

triglyceride   phosphoric acid   phospholipid

The phospholipid structure above is normally shown as in the diagram below.

This is the polar head.
It attracts water.
This means it is **hydrophilic**.

These are fatty acid tails.
They repel water.
This means they are **hydrophobic**.

a phospholipid

Saturated and unsaturated fats

saturated fats	unsaturated fats
formed from saturated fatty acids	formed from unsaturated fatty acids
have no C=C (double bonds) in their hydrocarbon chains	have C=C (double bonds) in their hydrocarbon chains
people try to avoid eating them, as they can result in blocked blood vessels	are part of a healthier diet

Examiner's Tip

In an exam you may be given the structure of a triglyceride and be asked to show its conversion to glycerol and fatty acids. Remember that knowledge of the reverse reaction can also be tested.

Proteins

- Always contain the elements **carbon**, **hydrogen**, **oxygen** and **nitrogen**.
- Usually **sulphur** is present as well as iron and phosphorus.
- Are formed from a number of repeated units, **amino acids**.

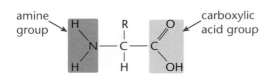

an amino acid

How is a protein constructed?

- Amino acids bond together by **peptide bonds**.
- Many amino acids bond together to form a long chain, a **polypeptide**.
- Different amino acid sequences result in different polypeptides.
- These precise sequences are controlled by an organism's DNA.
- This linkage of amino acids takes place during protein synthesis.
- Different organisms produce different polypeptides.

A peptide link formed by two amino acids is shown in the diagram.

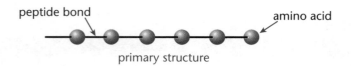

The structure of proteins

Primary protein structure

This is the **linear sequence** of amino acids along a polypeptide.

peptide bond   amino acid

primary structure

Peptide bonds can be broken down by peptidases. Exopeptidases break down bonds on the outside of a polypeptide. Endopeptidases break down the inner peptide bonds.

Secondary protein structure

There are two possible **secondary structures**.

1 **α-helix** – a tight, twisted polypeptide strand.

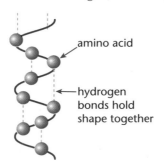

2 **β-pleated sheet** – adjacent polypeptides bond with the next, and so on, to form a sheet or ribbon shape. The polypeptides are held in position by hydrogen bonds.

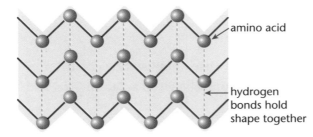

In both α-helices and β-pleated sheets, a hydrogen bond forms between the C=O of one amino acid and the H–N of an adjacent amino acid, like this: C=O---H–N.

Tertiary protein structure

This is the **folding** of a polypeptide into a **precise** shape. The polypeptide is held in 'bends' and 'tucks' in a **permanent** shape by a range of bonds, including:

- **disulphide** bridges (strong covalent bonds formed between adjacent Sulphur atoms)
- hydrogen bonds (weak bonds, hydrogen atom is shared by two other atoms)
- ionic bonds (weak electrostatic links between oppositely charged ions)

The bonds stabilise the tertiary structure of the protein. Additionally hydrophobic side chains on non-polar amino acids exclude water.

Quaternary protein structure

Some proteins consist of **different polypeptides** bonded together to form intricate shapes. A protein containing two or more polypeptides has a quaternary structure.

a quaternary structure

Biochemical tests

Different types of protein

Haemoglobin

- is found in red blood cells
- is a globular protein
- consists of four polypeptide chains
- two polypeptides are α-helix chains and two are β-pleated sheet chains
- each polypeptide is attached to a haem group, which contains iron
- each haem group has a binding site suitable for the transport of an oxygen molecule
- each haemoglobin molecule can carry up to 4 oxygen molecules
- oxygen can be transported on the haem group then be off-loaded at the tissues.

Collagen

- is a fibrous protein
- is a helix in shape, formed from three twisted polypeptide chains
- achieves stability from the hydrogen bonds between adjacent –NH and –CO groups
- is a molecule which resists stretching
- is a major part of tendons so that the pulling force of the muscle is efficiently transferred to a bone.

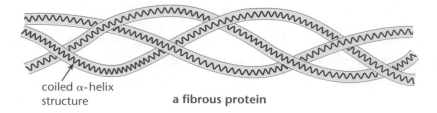

coiled α-helix
structure

a fibrous protein

Collagen is a major structural protein and is found in connective tissues which hold organs together. Tendons are connective tissues as well as bone. The structure of collagen is very different to the intricate folding of haemoglobin, which has a transport function.

All enzymes are proteins. Would you expect enzymes to be fibrous or globular?

Try to think of a reason for your choice.

Examiner's Tip

The four protein structures are often examined, as well as protein synthesis. The tertiary structure folding of polypeptides gives the precise shape which forms the active site of enzymes. All enzymes are proteins.

AS Biology Revision Notes

Biochemical tests

Tests for carbohydrates in the laboratory

Benedict's test

Used to test for reducing sugars (monosaccharides and some disaccharides).

- Add Benedict's solution to the chemical sample and heat.
- The solution changes from blue to brick red or yellow if a reducing sugar is present.
- The test is semi-quantitative as it gives a rough guide to the amount of reducing-sugar present.

Non-reducing sugar test

green   yellow   orange   brick-red

$\longrightarrow$

increasing amount of reducing sugar

Used to test for non-reducing sugars, e.g. the disaccharide, sucrose.

- First a Benedict's test is performed.
- If the Benedict's test is negative, the sample is hydrolysed by heating with hydrochloric acid, then neutralised with sodium hydrogen carbonate.
- This breaks the glycosidic bond of the disaccharide, releasing the monomers.
- A second Benedict's test is performed which will be positive because the monomers are now free.

Starch test

- Add iodine in potassium iodide to the sample.
- If starch is present the colour changes to blue–black.

Test for lipids in the laboratory

Emulsion test

Used to identify fats and oils.

- Add ethanol to the sample, shake, then pour the mixture into water.
- If fats or oils are present, a white emulsion appears at the surface.

Test for protein in the laboratory

Biuret test

- Add dilute sodium hydroxide and dilute copper sulphate to the sample.
- A violet colour appears if a protein is present.

Examiner's Tip

Always learn the complete range of biochemical tests. In exams you will probably be tested on at least one of them. It will be part of a bigger experiment. If you know a test it may help you understand the **whole** question!

The importance of water to life

Water is essential to living organisms. The list below shows some of its properties and uses.

- **Hydrogen bonds** are formed between the oxygen of one water molecule and the hydrogen of another. As a result of this water molecules attract each other. This is **cohesion**.

- **Cohesion** is responsible for surface tension which enables aquatic insects like pond skaters to walk on a pond surface. It also aids capillarity (the way in which water moves through the xylem in plants).

- Water is a **dipolar** molecule, which means that the oxygen has a slight negative charge at one end of the molecule, and each hydrogen a slight positive charge at the other end.

- Other **polar** molecules dissolve in water. The different charges on these molecules enable them to fit into water's hydrogen bond structure. Ions in solution can be transported or can take part in reactions. Polar substances, which dissolve are **hydrophilic**; non-polar substances, which cannot dissolve in water are **hydrophobic**.

- Water is used in **photosynthesis**, so it is responsible for the production of glucose. This in turn is used in the synthesis of many chemicals.

- Water helps in the **temperature regulation** of many organisms. It enables the cooling down of some organisms. Owing to a high **latent heat of vaporisation**, large amounts of body heat are needed to evaporate a small quantity of water. Organisms like humans cool down effectively but lose only a small amount of water in doing so.

- A relatively high level of heat is needed to raise the temperature of water by a small amount due to its **high specific heat capacity**. This enables organisms to control their body temperature more effectively.

- Water is a solvent for ionic compounds. A number of the essential elements required by organisms are obtained in ionic form, e.g.:

  (a) plants absorb nitrate ions (NO_3^-) and phosphate ions (PO_4^-) in solution

  (b) animals take in sodium ions (Na^+) and chloride ions (Cl^-).

Why are minerals important? They are vital to the life processes of organisms. The table below shows the roles of minerals.

mineral	animals	plants
calcium (Ca^{2+})	used for bones and teeth, and in muscle contraction	used to form healthy growing tips (apical meristems)
sodium (Na^+)	helps nerve and muscle function	
magnesium (Mg^{2+})	used in bones and enzymes responsible for energy release	used to make chlorophyll
nitrate NO_3^-	used to make protein	used to make protein
phosphate PO_4^-	used in ATP	aids root growth, used in ATP
potassium (K^+)	helps nerve and muscle function	helps form chlorophyll

Examiner's Tip

Water molecules are very important to many processes of living organisms. Absence of water would prevent absorption, transport, heat control and many other processes.

Progress check

1 **a** Complete the equation to show how the peptide bond of the molecule below forms two amino acids.

peptide bond

$$H-N-C-C-N-C-C \quad + \text{ molecule X} \longrightarrow$$

b **i** State the type of reaction which takes place when the molecule shown above forms two amino acids.

  ii Name molecule X.

2 The statements below refer to the possible structures of a protein.

   a A polypeptide is folded together in a precise shape.
   b Different polypeptides are bonded together to form intricate shapes.
   c A sequence of amino acids is coiled to form an α-helix.
   d Amino acids on adjacent polypeptides bond to form a β-pleated sheet.
   e A linear sequence of amino acids.

Write down *one* number: 1 (primary), 2 (secondary), 3 (tertiary) or 4 (quaternary) to show the correct structure.

3 The diagram below shows a phospholipid.

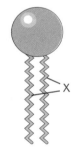

a phospholipid

   a **i** Name the parts labelled X.
     ii These parts of the phospholipid are hydrophobic. What does this mean?
   b The polar head is hydrophilic. What does this mean?

4 A non-reducing sugar is identified by a combination of:
   • Benedict's test
   • hydrolysis by heating with dilute hydrochloric acid.
   Explain how both processes can be used to identify a non-reducing sugar.

Answers on page 91

Cells

The animal cell and its organelles

The ultra-structure of cells

Sub-cellular units are called organelles and can be seen by using an electron microscope. Each organelle has been researched to help us understand more about the processes of life. Each organelle in a cell is suspended in a semi-liquid medium, the cytoplasm. Many ions are dissolved in it. It is the site of many chemical reactions.

The diagram shows the organelles found in a typical animal cell.

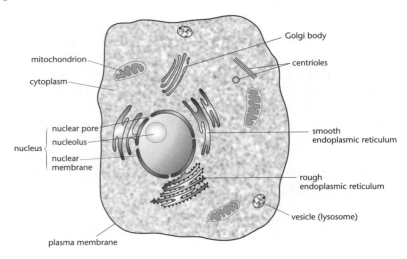

Cell surface (plasma) membrane

- This covers and protects the outside of a cell.
- It is a double layered sheet of phospholipid molecules with proteins.
- It is selective, allowing the import and export of chemicals and preventing entry of others.

Some cells have hair-like structures called cilia on the cell surface membrane which can move to and fro, like a corn field in a breeze. They have an internal structure of tubules in a 2 (central) and 9 (outer) pattern. They allow substances to be moved, e.g. mucus in the trachea is used to transport dust.

Nucleus

- This controls cell activity using coded instructions.
- Coded instructions in DNA enable the cell to make specific proteins.
- The nucleus stores, replicates and decodes DNA.
- The nuclear envelope is a double membrane layer having many pores.

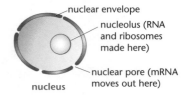

AS Biology Revision Notes

Mitochondrion

- The cristae and matrix contain enzymes to carry out aerobic respiration.
- It is the key organelle in release of energy, making ATP available to the cell.
- Mitochondria are needed for many energy requiring processes in the cell, including active transport and the movement of cilia.

Ribosomes

- These are located along **rough endoplasmic reticulum**.
- They aid the manufacture of proteins.
- They are the site where mRNA meets tRNA so that amino acids are bonded together.

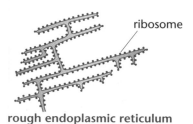

rough endoplasmic reticulum

Endoplasmic reticulum (ER)

- This is a series of folded internal membranes.
- **Rough ER has ribosomes.**
- **Smooth ER does not have ribosomes.**
- Substances are transported in the spaces between the ER.
- It is the site of many enzymicalley controlled reactions

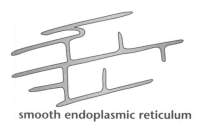

smooth endoplasmic reticulum

Golgi body

- This packages chemicals in membrane bound sacs which pinch off to make vesicles.
- It aids the production and secretion of many substances.
- Vesicle membranes merge with the plasma membrane to enable secretions to take place.

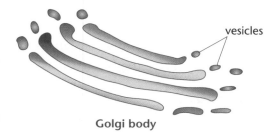

Golgi body

Centrioles

- These are two short cylinders which contain **microtubules**.
- During cell division they move to opposite poles as the spindle develops.

Lysosomes

- are small spherical vesicles
- contain digestive enzymes
- are needed to isolate the enzymes otherwise other organelles would be attacked
- release the enzymes at an appropriate time.

Examiner's Tip

Remember that organelles work together in groups, e.g. the nucleus and ribosomes work together in protein synthesis.

The plant cell and its organelles

All of the structures described for animal cells are also found in plant cells. Additionally there are three extra structures as shown in the diagram below.

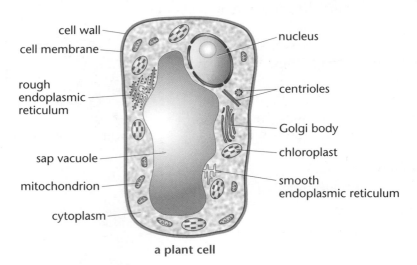

a plant cell

Cell wall

- This is located around the plasma membrane of plant cells.
- It consists of cellulose in a layer of calcium pectate and hemicelluloses.
- Calcium pectate cements one cell to the next in multi-cellular plants.
- It provides a rigid support for the cell.
- It allows many substances to be imported or exported.
- It allows the cell to build up an effective hydrostatic skeleton.

Chloroplast

- This enables the plant to photosynthesise, making glucose.
- It consists of an outer covering of two membranes.
- Inside the chloroplast are more membranes stacked in piles called **grana**.
- The membranes enclose a substance vital to photosynthesis, chlorophyll.
- Inside the chloroplast is a matrix known as the **stroma**, also involved in photosynthesis.

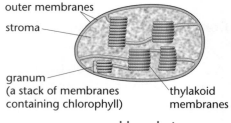

a chloroplast

Sap vacuole

- This is a large space in a plant cell.
- It contains the sap (chemicals including mineral ions in water).
- It is surrounded by a membrane known as the **tonoplast**.
- It contains enough water to maintain internal hydrostatic pressure. When this is achieved the cell is turgid, having maximum hydrostatic strength.

Examiner's Tip

Remember that plant cells have all the organelles also found in animal cells plus three different parts: cell wall, chloroplasts and sap vacuole.
(Remember that not all plant cells possess chloroplasts!)

Prokaryotic and eukaryotic cells

Organisms can be classified into two groups, **prokaryotic** or **eukaryotic** according to their cellular structure. Prokaryotic cells are less complex than the eukaryotic ones and are considered to have evolved earlier. The table below states similarities and differences between the two types of organism.

	prokaryotic cells	eukaryotic cells
kingdom	**Prokaryotae**	**Protoctista, Fungi, Animalia, Plantae**
organelles	small ribosomes	large ribosomes
	DNA present but there is no nuclear membrane	DNA is enclosed in a membrane, i.e. has nucleus
	mitochondria not present	has mitochondria
	has no Golgi body, vesicles or ER	Golgi body, vesicles and ER are present
	cell wall present consisting of mucopeptides	cellulose cell walls present in plants – a chitin-like substance in the cell walls of many fungi – no cell walls in animals
	if cells have flagellae there is no 9+2 microtubule arrangement	if cells have flagellae there is a 9+2 microtubule arrangement

Examiner's Tip

You will often be given a diagram of a cell from an organism you have not seen before. The examiners are testing your recognition of the organelles and their function. Check out the organelles; this will enable you to classify the organism as prokaryotic or eukaryotic.

Tissues and organs

Most multicellular organisms are formed from tissues and organs.

Tissue

- is a group of cells of similar structure which together have a specific function
- is formed from cells of identical origin.

Example – Squamous epithelium

All epithelial cells are lining cells. Squamous epithelial cells line the alveoli of the lungs. The cells are flattened giving a short diffusion path and a high surface area. They are specialised in the exchange of substances.

Example – Ciliated epithelium

The cilia move to and fro, to move fluids across the cell surface membrane. Some unicellular organisms use cilia to move through water and some organisms create water currents to, for example, maximise gaseous exchange.

Some tissues consist of a mixture of different types of cell e.g. phloem tissue consists of two types of cell, the sieve tubes and companion cells (see page 51).

Organ

- Is a group of different tissues working together in a common function.

The heart consists of a range of tissues including cardiac muscle, nervous tissue, and connective tissue (see page 41).

The leaf consists of a range of tissues including palisade and spongy mesophyll, phloem and xylem (see page 35).

Electron and light microscopy

Microscopes rely on **magnification** and **resolution**.

- **Magnification** is number of times an image is bigger than the actual specimen.
- **Resolution** is the ability to distinguish between two objects as separate entities. At low resolution only one object may be detected. At high resolution two distinct objects are visible.

The electron microscope has much better magnification and better resolution than the light microscope. Which would you use to give greater detail?

The light microscope

- White light illuminates specimen.
- Light is focused onto the specimen by a **condensing lens**.
- Specimen is placed on a microscope slide which is clipped on to the stage.
- Image is viewed via an eyepiece lens.
- Image size is the magnification value of the eyepiece lens multiplied by the magnification value of the objective lens.

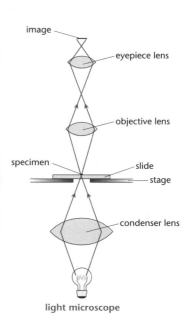

light microscope

The transmission electron microscope

- This uses an electron stream which is directed at the specimen.
- It has extremely high magnification and resolution.
- Specimens are placed in a vacuum within the microscope, otherwise the electrons would collide with air molecules.
- It uses **stains** such as **osmium** salts to make organelles distinct.
- Stains are absorbed by organelles and membranes differentially.
- Electrons are unable to pass through stained areas which show up as electron shadows on the screen.
- Cytoplasm allows more electrons to pass through, which reach the screen and lead to emission of light by fluorescence.

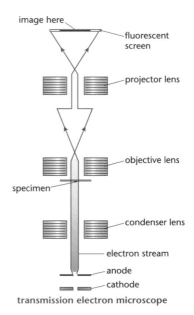

transmission electron microscope

Examiner's Tip

Artefacts are artificial changes in the material due to the preparation of the specimen. They are alien to the material which should not be interpreted as part of the specimen. One student thought air bubbles were eggs!

Calculating magnification

When you interpret a photomicrograph the image is much bigger then the specimen. The magnification is calculated by multiplying the magnification of the eye piece lens by the objective lens.

e.g. (1) eyepiece lens x 10

objective lens x 10

magnification = 10 x 10

x 100 (low power)

(2) eyepiece lens x 10

objective lens x 40

magnification = 10 x 40

= x 400 (high power)

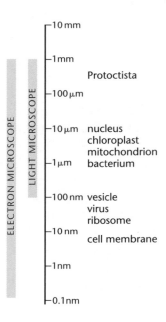

Progress check

1 Three of the following statements are false. Find and correct them.
   a   DNA is contained in the nucleus.
   b   The cell membrane consists of phospholipids and proteins.
   c   Ribosomes are found along the endoplasmic reticulum.
   d   Aerobic respiration takes place in the cytoplasm.
   e   mRNA is made in the ribosomes.
   f   The centrioles contain microtubules

2 The statements below describe features of *either* prokaryotic organisms *or* eukaryotic organisms. Write down P or E to show which is prokaryotic and which is eukaryotic.
   a   Nuclei present, which are membrane bound.
   b   Cells have flagellae without a 9+2 microtubule arrangement.
   c   No membrane bound organelles.
   d   Large ribosomes.

3 Describe how you would recognise each of the following organelles in an electron-micrograph:
   a   mitochondrion.
   b   lysosome.
   c   rough endoplasmic reticulum.

Answers on page 91

Enzymes

Enzymes in action

How enzymes work

Living cells carry out many biochemical reactions. These reactions take place rapidly due to the presence of enzymes. All enzymes consist of globular proteins which have the ability to 'drive' biochemical reactions. The ability of an enzyme to function depends on the specific shape of the protein molecule. The intricate shape created by polypeptide folding is a key factor in both theories of how enzymes work.

Lock and key theory

- Part of the enzyme has a cavity with a precise shape (active site).
- A substrate can fit into the active site.
- The active site (lock) is exactly the correct shape to fit in the substrate (key).
- The substrate binds to the enzyme, forming an enzyme–substrate complex.
- The reaction takes place immediately.
- Certain enzymes break a substrate down into two or more products (catabolic reaction).
- Other enzymes bond two or more substrates together to assemble one product (anabolic reaction).

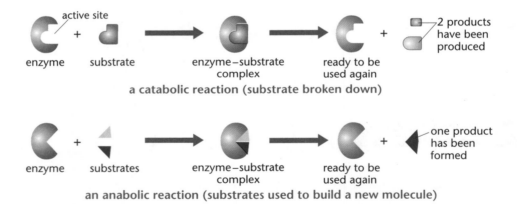

a catabolic reaction (substrate broken down)

an anabolic reaction (substrates used to build a new molecule)

An example of an enzyme in human cells is catalase.
The reaction it drives is shown by the equation below.

$$2H_2O_2 \rightarrow 2H_2O + O_2$$

Hydrogen peroxide → Water + Oxygen

Any of the toxic hydrogen peroxide produced in our cells is changed to harmless water and oxygen.

> **Is this an anabolic or catabolic reaction?**

AS Biology Revision Notes

Induced fit theory

- The active site is a cavity of a particular shape.
- Initially the active site is not the correct shape in which to fit the substrate.
- As the substrate approaches the active site the site changes and this results in it being a perfect fit.
- After the reaction has taken place, and the products have gone, the active site returns to its normal shape.

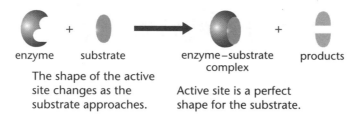

enzyme   substrate   enzyme–substrate complex   products

The shape of the active site changes as the substrate approaches.

Active site is a perfect shape for the substrate.

Active Site

Every enzume has an active site which is a precise shape. This means that enzymes are highly specific. Only a substrate of a particular shape will fit the actual site.

Lowering of activation energy

Every reaction requires the input of energy. Enzymes reduce the level of activation energy needed, as shown by the graph below.

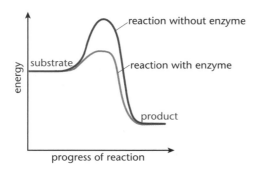

The higher the activation energy the slower the reaction. An enzyme reduces the amount of energy required for a biochemical reaction. When an enzyme binds with a substrate the available energy has a greater effect and the rate of catalysis increases. The conditions which exist during a reaction are very important when considering the rate of progress. Each of the following has an effect on the rate:

- concentration of substrate molecules
- concentration of enzyme molecules
- temperature
- pH.

Examiner's Tip

You may be questioned on the factors which affect the rate of reaction. Less able candidates tend to remember just one or two factors. Learn all four factors here and achieve a higher grade!

Effect of concentration and temperature

Effect of enzyme concentration

When considering the rate of an enzyme catalysed reaction the proportion of enzyme to substrate molecules should be considered. Every substrate molecule fits into an active site, then the reaction takes place. If there are more substrate molecules than enzyme molecules, then the number of active sites available is a limiting factor. The optimum rate of reaction is achieved when all of the active sites are in use. At this stage, if more substrate is added, there is no increase in rate of product formation. When there are less substrate molecules than enzymes the reaction will take place very quickly, as long as the conditions are appropriate.

Remember that other factors affect an enzyme catalysed reaction:

- substrate concentration • enzyme concentration • temperature.

Each can be a limiting factor, holding back the rate of the reaction.

Effect of temperature on an enzyme catalysed reaction

- Heat energy reaching the enzyme and substrate molecules causes them to increase random movement.
- The greater the heat energy, the more the molecules move and so collide more often.
- The more collisions there are the greater the chance that substrates will fit into an active site, up to a specific temperature.
- At the optimum temperature of an enzyme, the reaction rate is maximum.
- Heat energy also affects the shape of the active site, the active site being best at the optimum temperature.
- At temperatures above optimum, the rate of reaction decreases because the shape of the active site begins to change.
- Very high temperature causes the enzyme to become denatured, i.e. bonding becomes irreversibly changed and the active site is permanently damaged.
- At very high temperatures, the number of collisions is correspondingly high, but without active sites no products can be formed.
- At lower temperatures than the optimum, the rate of the reaction decreases because of reduced enzyme/substrate collisions.

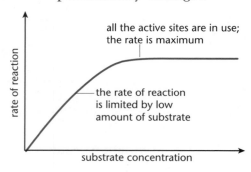

all the active sites are in use; the rate is maximum

rate of reaction

the rate of reaction is limited by low amount of substrate

substrate concentration

Rate of an enzyme catalysed reaction

This can be calculated by measuring

(a) how much product is formed per unit time

OR

(b) how much substrate has disappeared per unit time.

Examiner's Tip

The **pH** of the medium can have a direct effect on the bonding responsible for the **tertiary structure** of enzymes. If the active site is changed, then enzyme action will be affected. Each enzyme has an optimum pH.

Inhibition of enzymes

What are inhibitors?

If enzyme reactions inside the cell were to continue without regulation, there would be many problems. Cells possess **regulatory chemicals** which slow down or stop enzyme catalysed reactions. There are two types of inhibitor: competitive and non-competitive.

Competitive inhibitors

- These are molecules of **similar shape** to the normal substrate and are able to bind to the active site.
- They do not react within the active site, but leave after a time without any product forming.
- The enzymic reaction is **reduced** because while the inhibitor is in the active site, **no substrate can enter**.
- Substrate molecules **compete** for the active site so the rate of reaction decreases.
- The higher the proportion of competitive inhibitor the slower the rate of reaction.

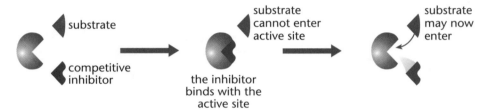

Non-competitive inhibitors

- These are molecules which bind to some part of an enzyme other than the active site.
- They have a different shape to the normal substrate.
- They change the shape of the active site which no longer allows binding of the substrate.
- Some substrate molecules may reach the active site before the non-competitive inhibitor.
- The rate of reaction is reduced.
- Finally they leave their binding sites, but substrate molecules do not compete for these, so they have a greater inhibitory effect.

(continued next page)

The graph below shows the relative effects of competitive and non-competitive inhibitors, compared to a normal enzyme catalysed reaction.

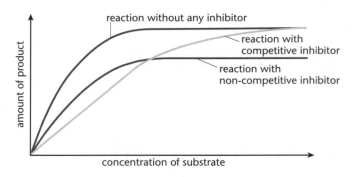

End product inhibition

This mechanism is needed to regulate certain enzyme catalysed processes in organisms. It involves allosteric sites. The diagram below shows one example of end product inhibition.

Stage 1

- A substrate binds with the active site of enzyme X.
- A product is formed.

Stage 2

- The product then binds with the active site of enzyme Y.
- Another product is formed.

Stage 3

- The stage 2 product then binds with the active site of enzyme Z.
- Another product is formed.

Stage 4

- This final product is the correct shape to bind with the allosteric site of enzyme X.
- Once in position it distorts the active site, inhibiting the first reaction.
- The final end product has caused its own decrease.

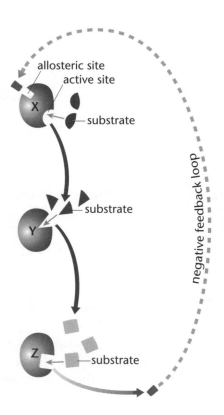

Examiner's Tip

Inhibitors are needed so that reactions are regulated. If too much product is made, then there are serious consequences. How does pH affect the rate of an enzyme catalysed reaction?

Home, medical and industrial applications of enzymes

Biological detergents

These are products such as biological washing and dishwasher powders. The common link between them is they contain a range of **hydrolysing enzymes** which invariably are:

- amylases – break down starch stains
- cellulases – break down the ends of damaged cotton fibres to remove the 'fuzz' produced during washing
- lipase – breaks down lipid stains into fatty acids and glycerol
- proteases – break down the many different proteins found in food stains.

This enzyme 'cocktail' has a low temperature optimum around 50°C, so that much less electricity is needed for washing; additionally, difficult stains are removed.

Fruit juice extraction

Crushing fruit such as apples releases juice, a valuable food product. Extraction of the juice is aided by an enzyme as follows.

- **Insoluble pectin** causes plant cell walls to adhere to adjacent cells.
- During storage pectin changes to a **soluble** form which **binds water strongly**.
- **Pectinase** is used to break down the pectin chains which **reduces** its water holding capacity.
- After pectinase treatment, crushing releases a greater yield of juice.
- The pectinase even clears the juice of 'cloudiness' caused by pectin.

Immobilised enzymes

After completion of an enzyme catalysed reaction enzymes are unchanged and can be used again. Unfortunately the enzymes can contaminate the product, as they can be difficult to separate out from the reaction mixture. For this reason **immobilised enzymes** have been developed. They are used as follows.

- Enzymes are attached to insoluble substances such as resins and alginates.
- These substances usually form membranes or beads and the enzymes bind to the outside.
- Substrate molecules readily bind with the active sites and the normal reactions go ahead.
- Immobilised enzymes are easy to recover, remaining in the membranes or beads.
- There is no contamination of the product by free enzymes.
- Expensive enzymes are reused.
- Processes can be continuous unlike batch, where the process is stopped for 'harvesting'.

Biosensors

- These are devices which are used to **detect specific molecules**.
- A sample is placed in contact with the biosensor.
- When enzymes are used in the '**detection membrane**', if the chemical being investigated is present, the molecules fit into the active sites of the enzyme.
- This causes a **transducer** to produce an **electrical signal**.
- The level of electrical signal is proportional to the level of chemical, so the device is **quantitative**.

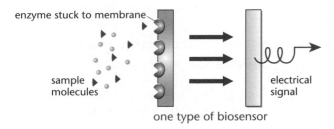

enzyme stuck to membrane

sample molecules

electrical signal

one type of biosensor

ELISA (enzyme-linked immunosorbent assay)

- This is used to detect minute quantities of protein in fluids such as blood plasma, if protein X, for example, is to be detected.
- Antibodies known to bind to protein X are fixed to a plate.
- Protein X, *if present*, binds to the antibody, whereas all other proteins wash away.
- A second type of antibody, linked to an enzyme, is added and binds to X at a different site to the first antibodies.
- A specific substrate is added which binds to the active site of this enzyme.
- The product formed is easily detectable, e.g. brightly coloured.
- This product would not form in the plate at all if protein X was absent.

Some diseases can be diagnosed by ELISAs, as specific proteins are detected in blood plasma. This technique has many applications including the detection of pregnancy, bacteria and viruses.

Clinistix

- These are strips of cellulose which have the enzyme **glucose oxidase** stuck to one end.
- When dipped into urine containing glucose the reaction produces **hydrogen peroxide**.
- This causes a **colour change** which signals that the patient is potentially diabetic.

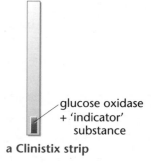

glucose oxidase + 'indicator' substance

a Clinistix strip

Examiner's Tip

Many new processes will be developed during the lifetime of your syllabus or specification. Remember to apply the principles of enzyme action to help you answer the question.

Progress check

1 The graph below shows the effect of an enzyme on the progress of a reaction.

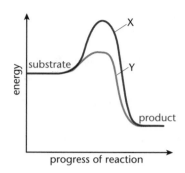

    a Which curve represents the reaction taking place with the enzyme? Give a reason for your answer.

    b Complete the sentence below.

       Enzymes increase the rate of reactions because they .... activation energy.

    c List *four* factors which effect the rate of an enzyme catalysed reaction.

2 Describe and explain the effect of the following on an enzyme catalysed reaction:

    a a competitive inhibitor

    b a non-competitive inhibitor.

3 **a** Describe *one* method of immobilising enzymes.

    b In a reaction catalysed by immobilised enzymes:

       i Why is there no contamination of the product?

       ii Why is it unnecessary to stop a process and keep it continuous?

4 The statements below explain how a biosensor can be used to detect specific molecules. The statements are in the wrong order. Give the correct sequence to show how the method works.

    a When enzymes are used in the **'detection membrane'**, if the chemical being investigated is present, the molecules fit into the active sites of the enzyme.

    b The level of electrical signal is proportional to the level of chemical, so the device is **quantitative**.

    c A sample is placed in contact with the biosensor.

    d This causes a **transducer** to produce an **electrical signal**.

Answers on page 92

Exchange

The cell surface membrane

How important is the surface area of exchange surfaces?

- Unicellular organisms have a very high surface area to volume ratio.
- All chemicals needed can pass into the cells directly and all waste can pass out efficiently.
- Organisms which have a high surface area to volume ratio have no need for special structures like lungs or gills.
- Nutrients and oxygen passing into an organism are rapidly used up, which limits the size to which a microorganism can grow.
- If vital chemicals did not reach all parts of a cell then death would be a consequence.
- Unicellular organisms satisfy all needs by direct diffusion.
- In larger organisms cells join to adjacent ones, which results in a lower surface area to volume ratio.
- Many large organisms have specially adapted exchange structures, all of which have a high surface area to volume ratio.

Fluid mosaic model of the cell surface (plasma) membrane

- Exchange of substances takes place across the cell surface membrane.
- It must be selective, to allow some substances in and exclude others.
- The cell membrane consists of a bilayer of phospholipid molecules.
- Each phospholipid is arranged so that the hydrophilic (attracts water) head is facing towards either the cytoplasm or the outside of the cell.
- The hydrophobic (repels water) fatty acid residues meet in the middle of the membrane.
- Across the phospholipids are a number of protein molecules.
- Some of the proteins (intrinsic) span the complete width of the membrane; some proteins (extrinsic) are partially embedded in the membrane.

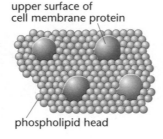

upper surface of cell membrane protein

phospholipid head

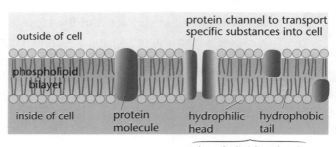

protein channel to transport specific substances into cell

outside of cell

phospholipid bilayer

inside of cell

protein molecule

hydrophilic head

hydrophobic tail

phospholipid molecule

The term 'fluid mosaic' was given because of the dynamic nature of the component molecules of the membrane. Many of the proteins seem to 'float' through an apparent 'sea' of phospholipids. Few molecules are static.

Functions of cell membrane molecules

Phospholipid

- Small lipid-soluble molecules pass through the membrane because they dissolve as they pass through the phospholipid bilayer.

- Small uncharged molecules also pass through the bilayer.

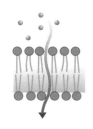

small lipid-soluble molecules pass through

Channel proteins (ion gates)

- Larger molecules and charged molecules can pass through the membrane due to channel proteins.

- Some are next to a **receptor protein**.

- This opens the channel protein or ion gate and ions flow through.

- Not all channel proteins need a receptor protein.

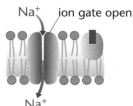

transmitter substance

receptor protein

Na⁺   ion gate open

Na⁺

Carrier protein molecules

- Some molecules which approach a cell may bind with a carrier protein.

- This has a site which the incoming molecule can bind to.

- This causes a change of shape in the carrier protein which deposits the molecule into the cell cytoplasm.

once in position the molecule changes the shape of the carrier protein

the site gives up the molecule on the inside of the cell

carrier protein

(continued next page)

Recognition proteins

- These are extrinsic proteins.
- Some have carbohydrate components.
- They help in cell recognition and cell interaction.
- For example, foreign protein on a bacterium would be recognised by white blood cells and the cell would be attacked.

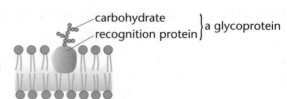

carbohydrate
recognition protein } a glycoprotein

Glycoproteins and glycolipids

Glycoproteins are found in all membrances and are protein molecules associated with carbohydrates, like the recognition protein above. Similarly glycolipids are lipid molecules associated with carbohydrates.

Glycoproteins

- These are protein molecules associated with carbohydrate chains.
- They are involved in the recognition of a cell as self or foreign.
- They may be involved in the uptake of specific substances by a cell.

Glycolipids

- These are lipid molecules associated with carbohydrate chains.
- They are found in cell membranes.
- They are found in higher numbers in the outer surfaces of neurones and chloroplast membranes.

Examiner's Tip

Take care with questions about channel proteins, e.g. insulin binds to a receptor protein, but it is glucose that enters the cell. (Not all channel proteins work in this way.)

The movement of molecules in and out of cells

The cell surface membrane is the key structure which forms a barrier between the cell and its environment. Nutrients, water and ions must enter and waste molecules must leave. Equally important is the exclusion of dangerous chemicals and inclusion of vital cell contents.

How do substances cross the cell surface membrane?

Cells obtain substances vital in sustaining life. Some cells secrete useful substances but all cells excrete waste substances. There are several mechanisms by which molecules move across the cell surface membrane.

Diffusion

Diffusion is the movement of molecules from where they are in high concentration to where they are in low concentration. Once evenly distributed the *net* movement of molecules stops. Molecules in liquids and gases are in constant random motion. When different concentrations are in contact, the molecules move so that they are in equal concentration throughout.

Factors which affect the rate of diffusion

- Surface area – the greater the surface area the greater the rate of diffusion.
- Difference in concentration at either side of the membrane – the greater the difference the greater the rate.
- Size of molecules – smaller molecules may pass through the membrane faster than larger ones.
- Presence of pores in the membrane – pores can speed up diffusion.
- Width of the membrane – the thinner the membrane the faster the rate.

Facilitated diffusion

- This is a special form of diffusion in which protein carrier molecules are involved.
- It is much faster than regular diffusion because of the carrier molecules.
- Each carrier will only bind with a specific molecule.
- Binding changes the shape of the carrier which then deposits the molecule into the cytoplasm.
- No energy is used in the process.

Osmosis

This is the movement of water molecules across a selectively permeable membrane:

- from a lower concentrated solution to a higher concentrated solution
- from where water molecules are at a higher concentration to where they are at a lower concentration
- from a hypotonic solution to a hypertonic solution
- from a hyperosmotic solution to a hypo-osmotic solution
- from an area of higher water potential to lower water potential.

selectively permeable membrane

- water molecule
- solute molecule

water molecules move from B to A

(continued next page)

What is the relationship between water potential of the cell and the concentration of an external solution?

- Water potential is a measure of water movement from one place to another in a plant.
- The units of pressure are usually kPa (kilopascals).
- Water potential is indicated by the symbol ψ (Greek letter psi).
- This equation allows us to work out the water 'status' of a plant cell.

$$\psi \text{ (cell)} = \psi_s + \psi_p$$

| water potential (of cell) | solute potential (of ions inside cell) | pressure potential (of cell wall) |

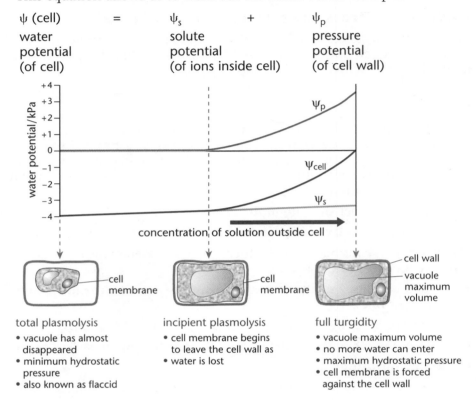

total plasmolysis
- vacuole has almost disappeared
- minimum hydrostatic pressure
- also known as flaccid

incipient plasmolysis
- cell membrane begins to leave the cell wall as
- water is lost

full turgidity
- vacuole maximum volume
- no more water can enter
- maximum hydrostatic pressure
- cell membrane is forced against the cell wall

Active transport

- Molecules move from where they are in lower concentration to where they are in higher concentration.
- A protein carrier molecule is used.
- This is against the concentration gradient.
- Energy is always required.

Endocytosis, exocytosis and pinocytosis

Some substances, often due to their large size, enter cells by endocytosis as follows.

- The substance contacts the cell surface membrane which indents.
- The substance is surrounded by the membrane, forming a vacuole or vesicle.
- Each vacuole contains the substance and an outer membrane which has detached from the cell surface membrane.

When fluids enter the cell in this way this is known as pinocytosis.

Some substances leave the cell in a reverse of endocytosis: exocytosis

Examiner's Tip

There are different ways of correctly defining osmosis. Be careful not to confuse them or you will lose marks.

Gaseous exchange

How are organisms adapted for efficient gaseous exchange?

- Larger organisms have a problem in exchange because of their low surface area to volume ratio.
- They have tissues and organs which have special adaptations for efficient exchange.
- In simple terms these structures achieve a very high surface area, e.g. a leaf; they link to the transport system to allow import and export from the organ.

A dicotyledonous leaf

A leaf has a high surface area over which exchange takes place. Specialised tissues increase the efficiency of exchange to allow photosynthesis to supply the plant with *enough* energy rich carbohydrates.

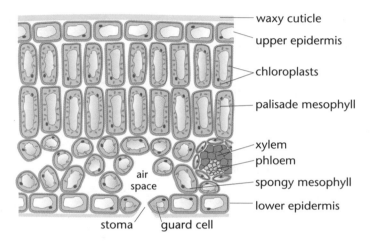

waxy cuticle
upper epidermis
chloroplasts
palisade mesophyll
xylem
phloem
air space
spongy mesophyll
lower epidermis
stoma
guard cell

Adaptations of a leaf for photosynthesis

- A flat, thin blade (lamina) to allow maximum light absorption.
- Cells of the upper epidermis have a waxy cuticle to reflect excess light, but allow entry of enough light for photosynthesis.
- Each leaf has many chloroplasts to absorb a maximum amount of light.
- Chloroplasts contain many thylakoid membranes, stacked in grana to give a high surface area to absorb the maximum quantity of light.
- Palisade cells, containing chloroplasts, pack closely together to 'capture' a maximum amount of light.
- Many guard cells open stomata to allow carbon dioxide in and oxygen out during photosynthesis.
- Air spaces in the mesophyll store lots of carbon dioxide for photosynthesis or lots of oxygen for respiration.
- Xylem of the vascular bundles brings water to the leaf for photosynthesis.
- Phloem takes the carbohydrate away from the leaf after photosynthesis.

(continued next page)

Gills of a bony fish

The ventilation mechanism of a fish allows intake of water, and passes it across the gills. The diagram below shows the structures of the gills which allow maximum exchange to take place.

Adaptations of gills for gaseous exchange

- The gills of a bony fish have a very high surface area to volume ratio.
- Gills consist of many flat gill filaments, stacked on top of each other, to give a high surface area for maximum exchange.
- Each gill filament has many gill plates which further increase surface area.
- Gill plates are very thin and full of blood capillaries to aid exchange.
- The gradients of O_2 and CO_2 are kept at a maximum by the **counter-current flow** mechanism. By allowing water to flow over the gills in an opposite direction to blood, maximum diffusion rate is achieved.

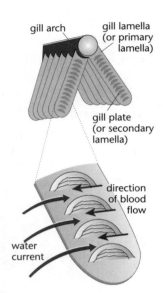

Lungs of a mammal

The ventilation mechanism of a mammal allows inhalation of air, which is passed into alveoli to exchange the respiratory gases. Completion of ventilation takes place when gases are expelled into the atmosphere. The diagram shows the structure of alveoli.

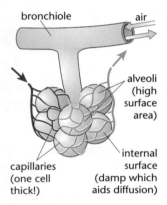

Adaptations of lungs for gaseous exchange

- Air flows through a trachea (windpipe) supported by cartilage.
- It reaches the alveoli via tubes known as bronchi and bronchioles.
- Lungs have many alveoli (air sacs) which have a high surface area.
- Each alveolus is very thin (diffusion is faster over a short distance).
- Each alveolus has many capillaries, each one cell thick, to aid diffusion.
- There are many blood vessels in the lungs to give a high surface area for gaseous exchange and transport of respiratory substances.

Gaseous exchange in lungs

Aided by the process of ventilation gaseous exchange takes place at the alveoli in the lungs. The distribution and properties of each part of the respiratory system contribute to the efficiency of the system.

Trachea

- this is strengthened by C-rings of cartilage
- they allow flexibility as the neck bends and prevent the collapse of the tube (this would prevent air flow!)
- goblet cells line the inside of the trachea, and secrete mucus which traps dust, bacteria and other debris
- cilia (of the epithelial lining) move the mucus plus dust to the back of the throat where it can enter the oesophagus.

Bronchi

- these are two tubes which leave the trachea, each serving a single lung
- they have less cartilage C rings and some smooth muscle

Bronchioles

- do not possess cartilage
- have a much smaller diameter than the bronchioles
- have a large amount of smooth muscle
- this is used to actively increase the diameter of each bronchiole during inspiration
- it is used to actively decrease the diameter of each bronchiole during expiration.

Alveoli

- are enclosed sacs which lead from the extreme end of each bronchiole
- the end of each bronchiole has many **alveoli clusters**, giving a massive surface area to volume ratio
- one cell thick **squamous epithelium** gives a very thin alveolus wall
- the epithelium of each alveolus produces **surfactant** which reduces surface tension which increases flexibility and stretching property of alveoli.

Blood supply to the lungs

- The pulmonary artery brings deoxygenated blood into the lungs, linking to millions of capillaries.
- In turn these link to the pulmonary vein which transports oxygenated blood back to the heart.

Human lung capacity

A **spirometer** can be used to measure the volume of air taken into the lungs and the volume of gases expelled. Changes are monitored by using a **kymograph**. A chart recorder is used to produce a graph as shown below.

As the chart recorder pen falls this measures the volume of air taken in. As the pen rises this shows the amount of gas breathed out.

Vital capacity

- is the maximum amount of air which can be expired after maximal inspiration (your deepest breath!).

Tidal volume

- is the amount of air inspired then expired in one breath
- tidal volume is at a minimum level during rest
- during exercise oxygen requirement is greater and the need to expel more carbon dioxide is greater, as a result tidal volume increases.

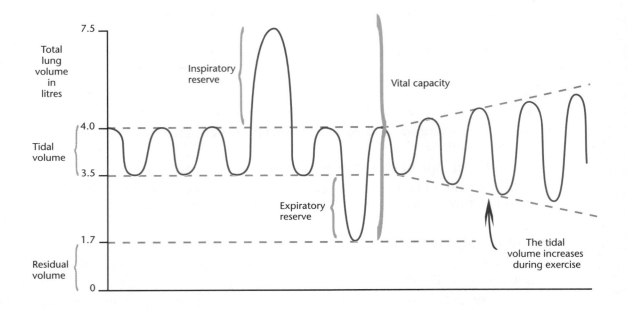

Examiner's Tip

Each of the respiratory surfaces in this section have common properties, such as high surface area to volume ratio, one cell thick lining tissue, many capillaries and damp surfaces. Many questions test your knowledge of these properties.

Progress check

1 The diagram below shows a channel protein (ion gate) and receptor protein in a cell surface membrane.

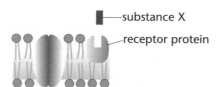 substance X

receptor protein

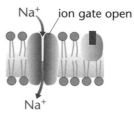 Na⁺ ion gate open

Na⁺

   a   Describe how molecule X can enter the cell with the help of both protein molecules.

   b   How do mitochondria help the process?

2 a   The following terms are used in the determination of water potential in cells:

ψ_p ψ (cell) ψ_s

      Rearrange the terms into an equation to enable the calculation of water potential of a cell.

   b   The water potential of plant **cell A** is –15 kPa. **Cell B** next to it is –20 kPa.

     i   Which cell would receive a net influx of water molecules?

     ii Name the process responsible for this movement.

     iii Complete the sentence.

      The cell membrane acts as a .... membrane.

3 a   Explain how a substance can enter a cell by the process of endocytosis.

   b   Suggest how a vesicle may be involved in the secretion of a substance by exocytosis.

Answers on page 92

EXCHANGE

Transport

Transport systems

Why do most multicellular organisms need a mass transport system?

- The bigger an organism is, the lower its surface area to volume ratio.
- Substances needed by a large organism could not be supplied through its exposed external surface.
- Oxygen passing through an external surface would be rapidly used up before reaching the many layers of underlying cells.
- Waste substances would not be excreted quickly enough.
- The problem has been solved, through evolution, by specially adapted tissues and organs.
- Leaves, roots, gills and lungs all have high surface area to volume properties.
- Supplies of substances vital to all the living cells are made available by these structures.
- Movement of substances to and from these structures is carried out by efficient mass transport systems.

Mass transport systems

Across the range of multicellular organisms found in the living world are a number of mass transport systems, e.g.:

- the mammalian circulatory system
- the vascular system of a plant.

Mass transport systems are important for:

- the rapid removal of waste, e.g. urea and carbon dioxide
- the supply of substances to tissues, e.g. glucose, oxygen and ions
- communication from one cell to another, e.g. hormones in the bloodstream.

The greater the metabolic rate of an organism, the greater are the demands on its mass transport system. Rapid movement through the transport system is improved by an organ which has a pumping mechanism. The heart is an excellent example of how this is achieved.

Double circulation

Mammals have a double circulation system.

- Blood enters the heart.
- It is then pumped to the lungs.
- Oxygen is exchanged for carbon dioxide.
- The blood returns to the heart.
- It is then pumped to the rest of the body.
- Blood therefore moves through the heart twice during each cardiac cycle.

Examiner's Tip

Double circulation has, through evolution, enabled some species to achieve a greater size because essential substances can reach cells and waste can be removed. The extra pumping action acts as a boost so that greater supply distances can be achieved.

The mammalian heart

- The most important heart tissue is cardiac muscle.
- Cardiac muscle cells contract and relax through the complete life of the person, without ever becoming fatigued.
- Each muscle cell is **myogenic**, i.e. has its own inherent rhythm. Below is a diagram of the heart.

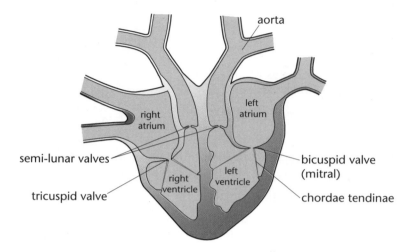

Structure

The heart consists of four chambers: right and left atria, and right and left ventricles. The functions of each part are as follows.

- The **right atrium** links to the **right ventricle** by the **tricuspid valve** (all valves prevent backflow of blood).
- The **left atrium** links to the **left ventricle** by the **bicuspid valve (mitral valve)**.
- The **chordae tendinae** attach each ventricle to its **atrioventricular valve**.
- Chordae tendinae hold each valve firmly to prevent the valve being pushed into an atrium (backflow of blood must be prevented!).
- **Semi-lunar (pocket) valves** are found in the blood vessels leaving the heart (pulmonary artery and aorta).
- Contraction of these arteries and relaxation of the ventricles closes each semi-lunar valve.
- Atria have thinner muscular walls than ventricles. When each atrium contracts it only needs to propel the blood a short distance into each ventricle.
- The left ventricle has even thicker muscular walls than the right ventricle, to propel blood to all of the body apart from the lungs.
- The right ventricle propels blood to the nearby lungs (the contraction does not need to be so powerful).

(continued next page)

Cardiac cycle

Blood is continuously being moved around the body, collecting and supplying vital substances to cells as well as removing waste from them. The heart acts as a pump using a combination of **systole** (contractions) and **diastole** (relaxation) of the chambers. The cycle takes place in the following sequence.

Stage 1: ventricular diastole, atrial systole

- Both ventricles relax simultaneously.
- Both atria contract simultaneously.
- Lower pressure in each ventricle compared to each atrium above slightly opens the atrioventricular valves.
- The atria contract which forces blood through the atrioventricular valves.
- Valves in the vena cava and pulmonary vein close.

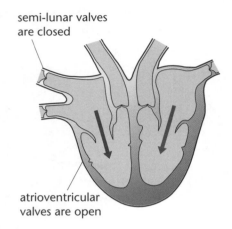

semi-lunar valves are closed

atrioventricular valves are open

Stage 2: ventricular systole, atrial diastole

- Both atria relax simultaneously.
- Both ventricles contract simultaneously.
- Atrioventricular valve closes due to higher pressure in the ventricles compared to the atria (prevents backflow of blood).
- Higher pressure in the ventricles compared to aorta and pulmonary artery opens the semi-lunar valves.
- Blood flows to the lungs and the rest of the body via the pulmonary artery and aorta.

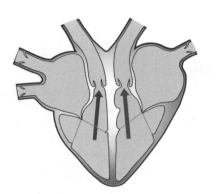

Stage 3: ventricular diastole, atrial diastole

- Ventricles and atria relax for a short time.
- Higher pressure in the aorta and pulmonary artery than the ventricles closes the semi-lunar valves.
- Higher pressure in the vena cava and pulmonary vein than the atria results in the refilling of the atria.

The cycle is now complete – GO BACK TO STAGE 1!

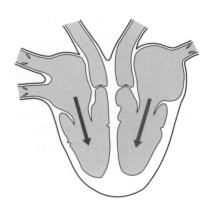

Examiner's Tip

Vigorous exercise is accompanied by an increase in heart rate to allow faster collection, supply and removal of substances because of enhanced blood flow. Conversely during sleep, at minimum metabolic rate, heart rate is correspondingly low because of minimum requirements by the cells.

Control of heart rate

Cardiac muscle cells have their own rhythm. Even so they must be coordinated, by electrical stimulation from the brain.

- The heart control centre is in the medulla oblongata.
- The sympathetic nerve stimulates an increase in heart rate.
- The vagus nerve stimulates a decrease in heart rate.
- These nerves link to a structure in the wall of the right atrium, the **sinoatrial node (SAN)**.
- A wave of electrical excitation moves across both atria.
- The atria respond by contracting (the right one slightly before the left).
- The wave of electrical activity reaches the **atrioventricular node (AVN)** which conducts the electrical activity through the **Purkyne fibres**.
- These Purkyne fibres pass through the septum of the heart deep into the walls of the left and right ventricles.
- The ventricle walls begin to contract from the apex (base) upwards.
- This ensures that blood is ejected efficiently from the ventricles.

The diagram below shows the electrical stimulation of the heart.

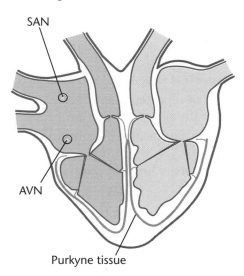

The SAN is the natural pacemaker of the heart. Sometimes it has to be replaced by an artificial, battery powered pacemaker. The hormone adrenaline has the effect of increasing heart rate and is produced in greater quantities in times of stress, e.g. during examinations!

(continued next page)

The following graphs show the changes in pressure and volume during the cardiac cycle.

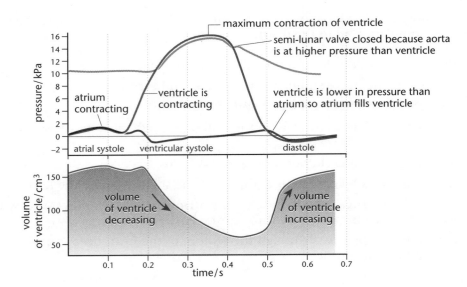

This is one of the examiner's favourite ways to test heart related concepts. Look at the **peak** of the **ventricular contraction**. It coincides with the **trough** in the **ventricular volume**. This is not surprising, because as the ventricle contracts it empties!

Some important points from the graphs:

- The time it takes for the complete cardiac cycle here is 0.7 seconds.
- In your exam, if you are shown a number of repeated heart cycles look for the pattern of one cycle and read off from the time axis.
- If adrenaline was present, then the time for one cardiac cycle would increase rapidly.
- The maximum ventricular pressure is when the ventricles contract (systole).
- The minimum ventricular pressure is when the ventricles relax (diastole).
- You can work out if a valve is open or closed in terms of pressure. Higher pressure above than below a semi-lunar valve closes it. Higher pressure below the semi-lunar valve than above, opens it.
- Higher pressure in the atria than the ventricles shows: the atria are contracting; the atrioventricular valves are open; and the ventricles are filling up with blood.

Examiner's Tip

In examinations you will often be given graphs which test your knowledge of the heart. Remember that the peak of one graph may correspond to the trough of another, e.g. the high pressure peak of a ventricle corresponds to its decreasing volume. It is emptying!

Blood vessels

Arteries, veins and capillaries

The blood is transported to the tissues via the vessels. Blood leaves the heart via arteries, reaches the tissues via the capillaries, then returns to the heart by the veins. Each blood vessel has a space through which the blood passes; this is the **lumen**.

Artery

- It has an outer covering of tough collagen fibres (**tunica externa**).
- It has a middle layer of **smooth muscle** and **elastic fibres** (**tunica media**).
- It has a lining of **squamous endothelium** (very thin cells).
- It can contract using its thick muscular layer.
- It transports blood away from heart under high pressure.
- Blood flow is rapid.

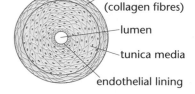

tunica externa
(collagen fibres)

lumen

tunica media

endothelial lining

Capillary

- It is a very thin blood vessel; the endothelium is just one cell thick.
- Substances can exchange easily.
- Pressure is lower than in the arteries.
- It has such a high resistance to blood flow that blood is slowed down (gives more time for efficient exchange of chemicals at the tissues).

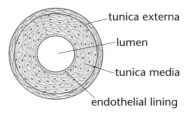

endothelium

lumen

Vein

- It has an outer covering of tough collagen fibres (**tunica externa**).
- It has a very thin middle layer of **smooth muscle** and **elastic fibres** (**tunica media**).
- It has a lining of **squamous endothelium** (very thin cells).
- It is lined with semi-lunar valves which prevent the backflow of blood.
- It transports blood towards heart under low pressure.
- Pressure lower than in capillaries
- Blood flow is slower.

tunica externa

lumen

tunica media

endothelial lining

How do the veins return the blood to the heart?

Veins have a thin muscle layer, so only mild contractions are possible. They return blood in an unexpected way. Every time the organism moves physically, blood is squeezed between skeletal muscles and forced along the vein. It must travel towards the heart because of the direction of the semi-lunar valves. Any attempt at backflow and the semi-lunar valves shut tightly!

direction of blood flow

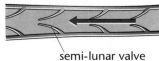

semi-lunar valve

(continued next page)

Capillary network

- Every living cell needs to be close to a capillary.
- Before blood from an artery enters into the capillaries it must pass through an arteriole.
- An arteriole has a ring of muscle known as a pre-capillary sphincter.
- Constriction of the arteriole shuts off blood flow to the capillaries.
- Dilation of the arteriole allows blood through into the capillaries.
- Some capillary networks have a shunt vessel.
- When the arteriole is constricted, blood is diverted along the shunt vessel so the capillary network is by-passed.
- After the capillary network has taken blood into an organ the capillaries link into a venule which joins a vein.

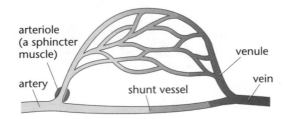

arteriole (a sphincter muscle)
venule
artery
shunt vessel
vein

In the skin the superficial capillaries have the arteriole/shunt vessel/venule arrangement as shown above. When the arteriole is dilated (vasodilation) more heat can be lost from the skin. When the arteriole is constricted (vasoconstriction) the blood cannot enter the capillary network and is diverted to the core of the body. Less heat is lost from the skin.

Blood

The blood consists of:

- **Plasma**, a fluid in which many solutes are dissolved and blood cells are suspended. (It is constantly circulated around the body and has a role in combating infections.)
- **Red blood cells**, which are biconcave to give a greater surface area to volume ratio for oxygen transport. A red blood cell has a nucleus when first formed but eventually the nucleus is lost. By this time around 90% of the cell is haemoglobin. Also contained in the cytoplasm is carbonic enhydrase which helps with carbon dioxide transport. (It is important that the blood has enough red blood cells and that each red blood cell contains enough haemoglobin to transport the oxygen efficiently.)
- **White blood cells**, which attack foreign proteins (antigens).
- **Platelets**, which have a major role in the clotting of blood.

Examiner's Tip

Be ready to relate the structure of blood vessels to their function, i.e. the greater amount of muscle of an artery gives it the ability to contract with greater force.

AS Biology Revision Notes

How is oxygen transported?

- Oxygen is absorbed in the lungs from air which has been breathed in.
- Red blood cells contain the protein **haemoglobin** which has an **affinity** (attraction) for oxygen.
- Even in short supply, oxygen will effectively bind with the haemoglobin to produce oxyhaemoglobin.
- Red blood cells have no nucleus, which increases surface area to volume ratio, so more oxygen is taken up.

Transporting the oxygen is very important. Equally important is the ability to **give up the oxygen to the tissues** which need it. The Bohr effect explains the way that oxygen moves from the red blood cells to the tissues.

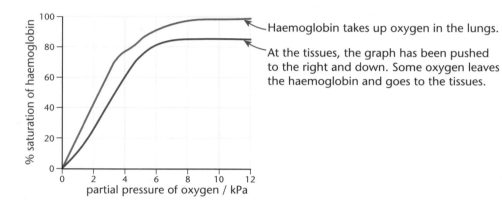

Haemoglobin takes up oxygen in the lungs.

At the tissues, the graph has been pushed to the right and down. Some oxygen leaves the haemoglobin and goes to the tissues.

Features of the Bohr effect

- The graph is known as the **oxygen dissociation curve** and its shape is sigmoid ('S' shaped).
- Even in a **low partial pressure** of oxygen, the **percentage saturation** of **haemoglobin** is **very high**, as shown by the steep incline on the graph at low partial pressures.
- Haemoglobin holds the oxygen strongly as the blood is transported.
- At the tissues, **carbon dioxide** in the red blood cells causes the dissociation curve to move downwards and to the right.
- The overall effect is that some oxygen is released from the haemoglobin and supplied to the tissues.
- The more carbon dioxide at the tissues, the more oxygen is 'off-loaded' to the tissues.

Fetal haemoglobin

Fetal haemoglobin has a greater affinity for oxygen than adult haemoglobin. In terms of the sigmoid graph above the curve for fetal haemoglobin is further to the left than for adult haemoglobin. This allows the fetus to take oxygen from the mother's haemoglobin.

Examiner's Tip

Always remember that CO_2 at the tissues causes the sigmoid curve to move to the right and some oxygen is offloaded from the haemoglobin to the tissues!

What is a closed circulation system?

Mammals have a closed circulation system of the heart plus continuous network of blood vessels.

The advantages of this are:
- Blood is pumped at a relatively high pressure.
- Flow rate is relatively fast.
- Organs are supplied by the vessels, specifically capillaries from which small amounts of fluid can escape.
- The fluid is known as tissue fluid which allows the exchange of chemicals between the organ and the blood.

Tissue fluid
- surrounds cells and exchanges substances with them
- consists of organic molecules, inorganic ions and water which leak from capillaries
- does not contain blood cells or proteins which are too big to escape through the capillary endothelium
- just before capillaries link to a vein water moves back into the blood which takes waste substances out of the tissue fluid.

Lymph
- is a fluid with components similar to those of tissue fluid
- is formed when tissue fluid moves from a capillary bed into the lymphatic vessels
- lipid molecules are added to the lymph at capillary beds along the small intestine

What is the effect of altitude on the blood?

The number of red blood cells in people can respond to changes in altitude as they travel around the world. Changes take place as follows:
- Air at sea level is more dense than at higher altitudes.
- People who live at lower altitudes therefore have more oxygen available per unit volume of air.
- Their bodies produce fewer red blood cells as a result.
- People who live at higher altitudes are adapted to produce a greater number of red blood cells.
- Having more red blood cells they can absorb enough oxygen from the "thinner" air.
- Athletes who reside at lower altitudes take advantage of this phenomenon.
- They live and train at a high altitude for several months.
- Their red blood cells increase in number dramatically.
- When they compete back at low altitudes they can absorb much more oxygen than normal.
- They may improve on performance!

Examiner's Tip

Athletes who reside at high altitudes would *not* have a similar benefit training at lower altitudes! In time their red blood cell numbers decrease.

The transport of substances in a plant

Root structure and functions

The roots of a green plant need to exchange substances with the soil environment. The root hair zone just behind a root tip has many root hairs which have a high surface area to volume ratio.

Root hairs

- are used for absorption of water and mineral ions
- have a cell membrane with a high surface area to volume ratio, in order to efficiently absorb substances such as water, mineral ions and oxygen
- are surrounded by soil water at high water potential compared to the low water potential of the contents of the root hairs
- have a cell membrane which is partially permeable to allow water absorption by osmosis
- have carrier proteins in the cell membranes to allow mineral ions to be absorbed by active transport.

Passage of water into the vascular system

Once absorbed by osmosis water needs to pass to the xylem vessels in order to move up the plant. First it must move across the cortex of the root and through the endodermis before entering the xylem. The mechanism of passage is not known but there are three theories:

- apoplast route, where the water is considered to pass on the outside of the cells
- symplast route, where the water is considered to pass via the cytoplasm of the cells through plasmodesmata (cytoplasmic strands connecting one cell to another)
- vacuolar route, where the water is considered to pass through the tonoplast, then through the sap vacuole of each cell.

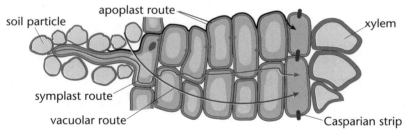

movement of water across the cortex

Movement of water across the cortex

Casparian strip

- Water moves across the cortex and must pass through the endodermal cells before entering the xylem vessels.
- Each cell of the endodermis has a waterproof band around it, just like a ribbon around a box.
- Water must pass through the cell in some way, rather than around the outside.
- If water moves by the apoplast route up to this point, then it must now move into the symplast or vacuolar pathways.

water must pass through middle of cell

Casparian strip (waterproof band)

Casparian strip of the endodermal cells

How does water move up the vascular system to the leaves?

Water moves into the **xylem** vessels (tube like structures) in the centre of the root; it enters via **bordered pits**. The xylem is internally lined with **lignin** which is waterproof and gives great strength to the xylem vessels. Much of the strength of a plant comes from cells toughened by lignin. Water moves up the xylem for the following reasons.

- Root pressure gives an upward force which helps water up the xylem vessels.
- Water continues up the xylem by capillarity which is the upward movement of a fluid through a narrow bore tube.
- Capillarity occurs because the water molecules have an attraction for each other (cohesion), so when one water molecule moves others move with it.
- Capillarity has another component; water molecules are attracted to the sides of the vessels which pulls the water upwards (adhesion).
- Transpiration causes a very negative water potential in the mesophyll of the leaves. Water in the xylem is of higher water potential and so moves up the xylem.

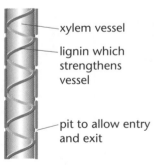

xylem vessel

lignin which strengthens vessel

pit to allow entry and exit

Examiner's Tip

Mineral ions are also transported in the xylem. Remember that the xylem is part of the mass flow system ensuring that all cells receive their requirements of water and minerals.

Translocation

- This is an **energy dependent process** by which **sucrose** and **amino acids** are transported through the phloem.
- Sugar is produced in the photosynthetic tissues and must be exported from these **sources** to areas of need.
- Areas needing large amounts of energy are called **sinks**, e.g. terminal buds and roots. (Roots cannot photosynthesise!)
- Sugars are transported in the phloem by translocation.

Structure of the phloem tissue

- A **sieve tube** links to the next via a **sieve plate** which is perforated with pores.
- The sieve tube has cytoplasm and a few small mitochondria.
- Sugars are thought to pass through sieve tubes by **cytoplasmic streaming**.
- Sieve tubes have no nucleus but are alive.
- Sieve tubes live because of cytoplasmic connections (**plasmodesmata**) with the companion cell.
- Each companion cell has a nucleus and many mitochondria.

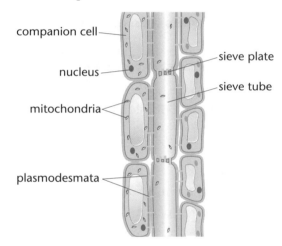

The sieve tube has no nucleus so that essential proteins for life are made by the companion cell which does possess a nucleus. The companion cell maintains services to the sieve tube.

The mechanism of translocation

Scientists are not sure how solutes move through the phloem. There are different hypotheses to explain the movement. Scientists are agreed that sucrose moves through the phloem more quickly than could be explained by diffusion. Additionally dead phloem, treated with hot wax, cannot translocate substances.

Pressure flow hypothesis

- Sieve tubes in a **leaf** have a high concentration of sucrose, giving a more negative water potential.
- Water flows into sieve tubes from adjacent xylem vessels, creating a **high** hydrostatic pressure.
- Sucrose is changed to starch in a root.
- As a result sieve tubes at the **root** have a low concentration of sucrose, giving a less negative water potential.

- Water flows out of sieve tubes into surrounding cells by osmosis giving a low hydrostatic pressure.
- A gradient of hydrostatic pressure is set up between the leaf and root.
- This results in a mass flow of water with dissolved solutes such as sucrose, from leaf to root.

Cytoplasmic streaming

- The cytoplasm moves through pores in the sieve plates found at each end of the sieve tubes.
- Radioactive labelling has tracked the movement of cytoplasm from one sieve tube to another.

Distribution of xylem and phloem

Plant cells gain mechanical strength from a combination of hydrostatic pressure and the cellulose cell wall. Xylem vessels are strengthened by **lignin**, a very tough substance. Even more important than the strength of individual cells is the distribution of the tissue.

The xylem is located in the leaf veins. The central vein is bigger where support requirement is greater. As a result the leaf lamina has both strength and flexibility.

The distribution of xylem is in the form of a cylinder. This gives flexible movement of the stem from side to side in wind. The xylem resists compression and extension.

The distribution of the xylem is in the form of a star shape on the middle of the root. This gives a counterbalanced resistance to stem movement.

Phloem allows the movement of sucrose and amino acids to areas of need. Buds and growing tips are the areas of greater mitotic cell division and so it is important that enough phloem tissue supplies these parts.

Radioactive labelling

This technique has been used to investigate the mechanism of translocation.

- It involves the use of a substance such as radioactive CO_2.
- A leaf is allowed to photosynthesise in the presence of $^{14}CO_2$ and makes the radioactive sugar ($^{14}C_6H_{12}O_6$).
- The route of the radioactive sugar can be traced using a Geiger–Müller counter.
- The greater the number of radioactive disintegrations per unit time, the greater is the concentration of the sugar in that part of the plant.

Water loss in a plant

How is water lost from a leaf?

- The process by which water is lost from any region of a plant is **transpiration**.
- Water can be lost from areas such as a stem, but most water is lost by **evaporation** through the **stomata**.
- Each stoma is a pore which can be open or closed and is bordered at either side by a guard cell.
- Some water can escape through the cell junctions and membranes; this is known as **cuticular transpiration**.
- In the dark all stomata are closed. Even so, there is still water loss by cuticular transpiration.

The diagrams show an open stoma and a closed stoma.

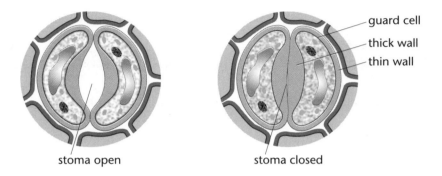

stoma open   stoma closed

guard cell
thick wall
thin wall

Transpiration from a leaf takes place as follows:

- The air spaces in the mesophyll become **saturated** with water vapour (**higher water potential**).
- The air outside the leaf may be of **lower humidity** (**more negative water potential**).
- Water molecules **diffuse** from the mesophyll of the leaf to the outside.

How do the guard cells open and close?

In the presence of light:

- K^+ ions are actively transported into the guard cells from adjacent cells.
- Malate is produced from starch.
- K^+ ions and malate accumulate in the guard cells.
- This causes an influx of water molecules.
- The cell wall of each guard cell is thin in one part and thick in another.
- The increase in hydrostatic pressure leads to the opening of the stomata.

Examiner's Tip

Closing of the stomata is the reverse of this process. Under different conditions the stomata can be partially open. The rate of transpiration can increase in warm, dry conditions or decrease in conditions at the opposite extreme.

Measuring the rate of transpiration

This is done indirectly using a potometer. This instrument works by the following principle: for every molecule of water lost by transpiration, one is taken up by the shoot.

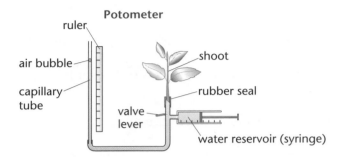

Potometer

ruler

air bubble

capillary tube

shoot

rubber seal

valve lever

water reservoir (syringe)

The potometer is used as follows:

- A shoot is cut and the end is quickly put in water to prevent an air lock in the xylem.
- The potometer is filled under water so that the capillary tube is full.
- All air bubbles are removed from the water.
- The shoot is put into the rubber seal.
- The valve is changed to allow water uptake.
- The amount of water taken up by the shoot per unit time is measured.
- The shoot can be tested under various conditions.

Xerophytes

These are plants which have **special adaptations** to survive in drying, environmental conditions where many plants would become desiccated and die. The plants survive well because of a combination of the following features:

- thick cuticle to reduce evaporation
- reduced number of stomata
- smaller and fewer leaves to reduce surface area
- hairs on plant to reduce air turbulence
- protected stomata to prevent wind access
- aerodynamic shape to prevent full force of wind
- deep root network to absorb maximum water
- some store water in modified structures, e.g. the stem of a cactus.

Examiner's Tip

In an exam you may be given a photomicrograph of a xerophytic plant which you have not seen before. Look for *some* of the features covered in the bullet points above.

Progress check

1 The diagram below shows a heart during the cardiac cycle.

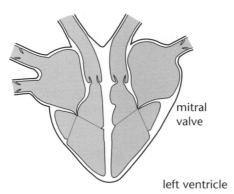

mitral valve

left ventricle

a Which of the statements are true?

i Blood is moving from the atria to the ventricles.

ii Blood is moving from the left ventricle through the aorta.

iii Blood is moving from the right ventricle through the pulmonary artery.

iv The atrioventricular valves are open.

v The semi-lunar valves are open.

vi The chordae tendinae are preventing the atrioventricular valves from pushing back into the atria.

b Complete the sentence.

Cardiac muscle has its own internal rhythm. The word which describes this is
…………….................. .

2 a The graph below shows the oxygen dissociation curve for myoglobin and haemoglobin.

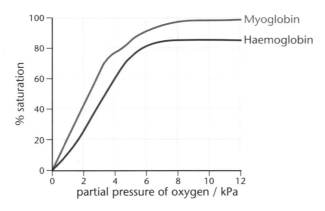

i Red blood cells with haemoglobin reach myoglobin in muscle cells. Referring to the graphs, explain what would happen to oxygen carried by the red blood cells.

ii What effect would carbon dioxide produced at the muscle cells have on the oxygen dissociation curve for haemoglobin?

b Which haemoglobin, fetal or adult, has a greater affinity for oxygen? Give a reason for your answer.

Answers on page 93

The genetic code

Chromosome structure and function

Chromosomes

Each chromosome in a nucleus consists of a series of genes. A gene is a section of DNA. Each gene controls the production of a protein important to the life of an organism.

Deoxyribonucleic acid (DNA)

DNA is made up of a number of **nucleotides** joined together in a double helix shape.

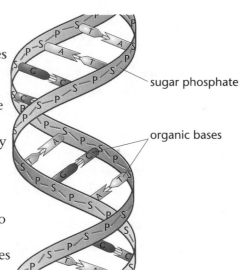

* The organic base of each nucleotide can be any one of adenine, thymine, cytosine or guanine.

sugar phosphate

* Nucleotides join together at their bases by hydrogen bonds.

organic bases

* Adenine bonds with thymine.

* Cytosine bonds with guanine.

* Phosphate and pentose sugar units link to form the sides of the DNA.

* The twisting pattern formed as nucleotides bond to each other is a double helix shape.

* Repeated linking of the monomer nucleotides forms the polymer, DNA.

Why does the DNA of one organism differ from the DNA of another?

* The answer lies in the **different sequences** of the organic bases along the DNA.

* Each sequence of bases is a code to make proteins, usually vital to the life of an organism.

A single nucleotide

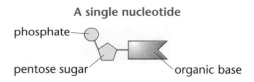

phosphate

pentose sugar

organic base

DNA

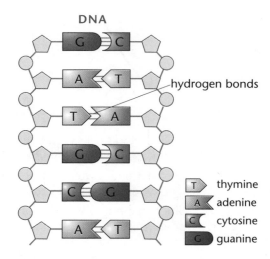

hydrogen bonds

T — thymine
A — adenine
C — cytosine
G — guanine

Examiner's Tip

Each strand of DNA is said to be complementary to the other. Be ready to identify one strand when given the matching complementary strand. Remember that adenine bonds with thymine and cytosine bonds with guanine.

AS Biology Revision Notes

How does a cell make protein?

This is called **protein synthesis**.

- Amino acids link in a chain sequence to form a **polypeptide**.

- A number of polypeptides can bond together to form a protein.

The diagrams show protein synthesis.

- In the nucleus, **RNA polymerase** links to a start code along a DNA strand.

- RNA polymerase moves along the DNA. For every organic base it meets along the DNA, a complementary base is linked to form mRNA (**messenger RNA**).

  Pairing of organic bases:
  DNA   G   C   T   A
  mRNA   C   G   A   U

- RNA polymerase links to a finish code along the DNA and finally the mRNA moves to a **ribosome**. The DNA stays in the nucleus for the next time it is needed.

- Every three bases along the mRNA make up one **codon** which codes for a specific amino acid. Three complementary bases form an **anti-codon** attached to one end of tRNA (**transfer RNA**). At the other end is a specific amino acid.

- All along the mRNA the tRNA 'partner' molecules enable each amino acid to bond to the next. A chain of amino acids (**polypeptide**) is made, ready for release into the cell.

Transcription

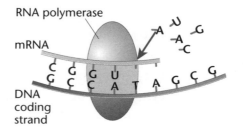
RNA polymerase

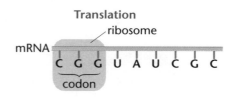
RNA polymerase
mRNA
DNA coding strand

Translation

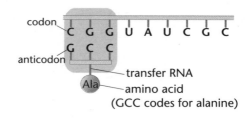
ribosome
mRNA
codon

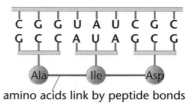
codon
anticodon
transfer RNA
Ala
amino acid
(GCC codes for alanine)

C G G U A U C G C
G C C A U A G C G
Ala   Ile   Asp
amino acids link by peptide bonds

Note the two parts to protein synthesis: transcription and translation. Be careful not to mix them up.

DNA codes

The table below shows:

- triplet sequences of organic bases found along DNA strands
- the coding function of each triplet.

During protein synthesis each triplet code results in specific amino acids being linked in chains known as **polypeptides**.

The coding strand of DNA codes for mRNA:

DNA:	A A A G A G G A C A C T	*(coding strand)*
mRNA:	U U U C U C C U G U G A	*(messenger RNA)*

Coding of bases:

- guanine (G) on DNA codes for cytosine (C) on mRNA
- cytosine (C) on DNA codes for guanine (G) on mRNA
- thymine (T) on DNA codes for adenine (A) on mRNA
- adenine (A) on DNA codes for uracil (U) on mRNA.

Special note: There is no thymine found on mRNA. Instead the organic base uracil is found.

Genetic code functions of DNA					
	second organic base				
	A	G	T	C	third organic base
A	AAA Phe	AGA	ATA Tyr	ACA Cys	A
	AAG	AGG Ser	ATG	ACG	G
	AAT Leu	AGT	ATT stop	ACT stop	T
	AAC	AGC	ATC stop	ACC Trp	C
G	GAA	GGA	GTA His	GCA	A
	GAG Leu	GGG Pro	GTG	GCG Arg	G
	GAT	GGT	GTT Gln	GCT	T
	GAC	GGC	GTC	GCC	C
T	TAA	TGA	TTA Asn	TCA Ser	A
	TAG Ile	TGG Thr	TTG	TCG	G
	TAT	TGT	TTT Lys	TCT Arg	T
	TAC Met	TGC	TTC	TCC	C
C	CAA	CGA	CTA Asp	CCA	A
	CAG Val	CGG Ala	CTG	CCG Gly	G
	CAT	CGT	CTT Glu	CCT	T
	CAC	CGC	CTC	CCC	C

Each triplet code is **non-overlapping**. This means that each triplet of three bases is a code, then the next three, and so on along the DNA. There are more triplet codes than there are amino acids. This is known as the **degenerate code**, because an amino acid such as leucine can be coded for by up to six different codes, e.g. GAG and GAC.

(continued next page)

Use this key to identify the amino acids in the table on the previous page.

amino acid	abbreviation	amino acid	abbreviation
alanine	Ala	lysine	Lys
arginine	Arg	methionine	Met
asparagine	Asn	phenylalanine	Phe
aspartic acid	Asp	proline	Pro
cysteine	Cys	serine	Ser
glutamine	Gln	threonine	Thr
glutamic acid	Glu	tryptophan	Trp
glycine	Gly	tyrosine	Tyr
histidine	His	valine	Val
isoleucine	Iso	leucine	Leu

Do not learn all of the different codes and functions of triplet codes. Be ready to use the supplied data in the examination. You will be given a key of different codes and functions. If you are given a table of codes check them carefully. If the bases are from mRNA then there will be uracil in the table.

Mutation

This is a change in the DNA of an organism. There are different effects on DNA causing different types of mutation. Here is a strand of DNA before mutation.

CTATCGCAAATACGT

Mutation type 1: CTATCGCAAATA**TGC**

This is **inversion**. The TGC triplet now codes for a different amino acid.

Mutation type 2: CTATCGCAAATACGT**CAA**

This is **addition**. The CAA triplet now codes for an extra amino acid.

Mutation type 3: CTATCGCAAATA

CGT is missing. This is **deletion**. One amino acid is missing from the polypeptide.

Mutation type 4

Large sections of DNA (whole chromosomes or sets of chromosomes) can be added.

One extra set of chromosomes gives a **triploid** number of chromosomes.

Examiner's Tip

Mutation types 1 to 3 are point mutation. They each affect one amino acid code. One base may change every amino acid code along the DNA, whereas one triplet may add **just one** amino acid. Which type of mutation do you think affects a protein the most?

Cell division

How do cells prepare for division?

Before cells divide they must first make an exact copy of their DNA by using a supply of organic bases, pentose sugar molecules and phosphates. This is known as the semi-conservative replication of DNA. DNA replication takes place before cell division in interphase.

The following diagram shows replication.

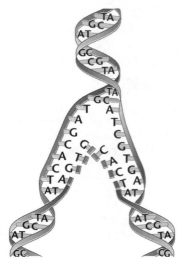

- DNA unwinds, exposing its two single strands.
- Each complementary strand then acts as a template to build its opposite strand.
- This results in the production of two identical copies of double stranded DNA.

Semi-conservative replication of DNA

What does semi-conservative mean? The answer lies in the results of this experiment carried out by researchers.

- Bacteria were cultured with a radioactive isotope of nitrogen in the organic bases of their DNA.
- The bacteria were then supplied with non-radioactive bases.
- They replicated their DNA using these bases as they reproduced.
- Each molecule of DNA of the next generation had one radioactive strand and one normal strand.

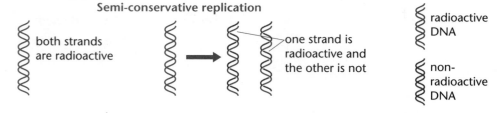

Semi-conservative means that as DNA splits into its two single strands, *each* of the new strands is made of newly acquired bases. The other strand, part of the original DNA remains.

Examiner's Tip

Be ready to analyse photomicrographs of all phases of mitosis. If you can spot 10 pairs of chromosomes at the end of telophase, then this is the original diploid number of the parent cell.

Process of cell division

Cells divide for the purposes of growth, repair and reproduction. Not all cells can divide but there are two ways in which division may occur, i.e. mitosis and meiosis.

Just before either mitosis or meiosis begins, **interphase** takes place. This is when the DNA of the chromosomes replicates. The sequence of diagrams below shows a cell dividing into two daughter cells by mitosis.

1 Prophase

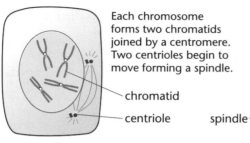

Each chromosome forms two chromatids joined by a centromere. Two centrioles begin to move forming a spindle.

chromatid

centriole

2 Metaphase

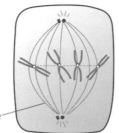

The chromatids, still joined by a centromere move to middle of cell. Each of the two chromatids has identical DNA to the other.

spindle

3 Anaphase

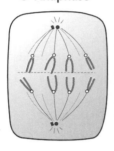

The spindle fibres join to the centromeres. The spindle fibres shorten and the centromeres split. The separated chromatids are now chromosomes.

4 Telophase

Identical chromosomes move to each pole. The nuclear membrane re-forms. The cell membrane narrows at the middle and two daughter cells are formed.

Homologous pair of chromosomes

The table below shows differences between mitosis and meiosis.

	mitosis	meiosis
How many daughter cells are produced?	2	4
Are the daughter cells identical or different to the parent cell?	identical (clones)	different
Are the chromosomes of daughter cells single or in pairs?	in pairs (diploid)	single (haploid)

Mitosis is the form of cell division responsible for **growth** and **repair**.

Homologous pairs

Chromosomes are found in homologous pairs. In humans one chromosome of the pair comes from each parent. Along each chromosome the genes are the **same** but at each gene it may be a different allele e.g. blue eyes and brown eyes.

Examiner's Tip

You will often be given a diagram or photomicrograph of one stage of mitosis. Be ready to identify it! For example, if the chromatid pairs are lined up at the equator it is metaphase.

Gene technology

Manipulating DNA

Scientists have developed methods of manipulating DNA.

- It can be transferred from one organism to another.
- Organisms which receive the DNA then have the ability to produce a new protein.
- This is one example of genetic engineering.
- Changes in the DNA of an organism by a range of methods use the knowledge and skills acquired during research into gene technology.

Gene transfer

The gene which produces human insulin was transferred from a human cell to a bacterium. The new microbe is known as a **transgenic bacterium**. The process which follows shows a similar technique.

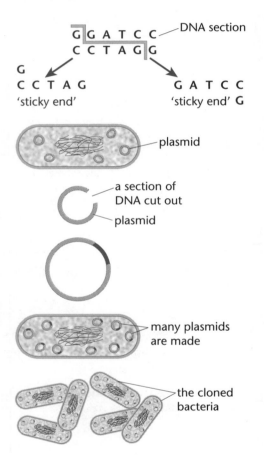

- An enzyme known as a **restriction endonuclease** cut the DNA and the gene was removed. Each time a cut was made the two ends produced were known as 'sticky ends'.
- Circles of DNA called **plasmids** are found in bacteria.

    A plasmid was taken from a bacterium and cut with the same restriction endonuclease.

- The human gene was inserted into the plasmid. It was made to fix into the open plasmid by another enzyme known as **ligase**.
- The plasmid **replicated** inside the bacterium.
- Large numbers of the new bacteria were produced. Each was able to secrete perfect human insulin, helping diabetics all over the world.

Examples of gene transfer

- The above method was used to transfer the gene for the production of insulin from a human nucleus into bacteria.
- Human insulin can now be produced by bacteria.
- Similarly the gene to produce factor VIII, essential for the clotting of blood, has been transferred to bacteria.

Modern industrial fermenters

Transgenic bacteria are cultured in huge industrial **fermenters**, like the one below. They secrete their products which can be collected. Many microbes are exploited in this way. The enzymes found in biological washing powders are produced by this method. The exploitation of microbes for human use is known as **biotechnology**.

- Fermenters are used to grow microorganisms on a large scale.

- They all have the common purpose of producing food, or chemicals such as antibiotics, hormones or enzymes.

The fermenter below shows a typical design.

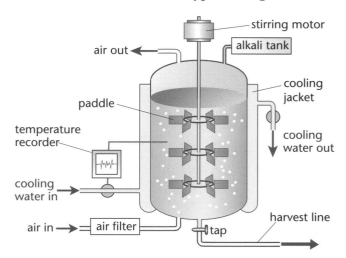

Conditions inside fermenters should be suitable for the optimal metabolism and rapid reproduction of the microorganisms. Products should be harvested without contamination. Note the conditions which need to be controlled.

- Fermenters are sterilised using steam before adding nutrients and the microorganisms used during the process. Conditions are **aseptic**.

- Nutrients which are *specifically* suited to the needs of the microorganisms are supplied.

- Air is supplied if the process is aerobic. This must be filtered to avoid contamination from other microorganisms.

- Temperature must be regulated to keep the microorganisms' enzymes within a suitable range. An active 'cooling jacket' and heater, both controlled via a thermostat, enable this to be achieved.

- pH must remain close to the optimum. Often the development of low pH during fermentation would result in the process slowing down or stopping. The addition of alkaline substances allows the process to continue and maximises yield.

- Paddle wheel mixing or 'bubble agitation' ensure that the microorganisms meet the required concentrations of nutrients and oxygen.

Examiner's Tip

In exams you may experience questions on a wide range of applications. New transgenic organisms are continually being developed. Many hit the headlines in the media. Be aware that the examiners may use these high profile organisms in questions. Do not become disorientated – the principle of genetic engineering are the same.

Electrophoresis

Restriction endonucleases can be used to cut up an organism's DNA.

- DNA sections are put into a well in a slab of agar gel.
- Electrodes apply an electrical field.
- DNA moves towards the anode.
- Smaller pieces of DNA move more quickly.
- Larger ones move more slowly, leading to the formation of bands (just like a bar code!).

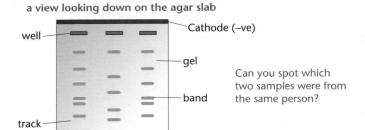

a view looking down on the agar slab

Cathode (–ve)
well
gel
band
track
A B C
Anode (+ve)

Can you spot which two samples were from the same person?

Genetic fingerprinting

Electrophoresis has many applications.

- Bands produced for an organism's DNA are distinctive and can help with identification.
- In some crimes DNA is left at the scene; blood and semen both contain DNA specific to an individual.
- DNA evidence can be checked against samples from suspects. This is known as genetic fingerprinting.
- Genetic fingerprinting can be used in paternity disputes because each band of the DNA of the child must correspond with a band from *either* the father or mother.
- Genetic fingerprinting is applied to organisms other than humans, e.g. illegal egg collectors have been successfully prosecuted when egg DNA has been compared against the DNA profile of parent birds.

Isolating genes

Scientists can identify and isolate a useful gene using the enzyme **reverse transcriptase**.

Stage 1		
When a polypeptide is about to be made at a ribosome, reverse transcriptase allows a strand of its coding DNA to be made	mRNA	UAA GCC GAU
	single DNA	ATT CGG CTA
Stage 2		
The single stranded DNA is parted from the mRNA	single DNA	ATT CGG CTA
Stage 3		TAA GCC GAT
The other strand of DNA is assembled using DNA polymerase	DNA	
		ATT CGG CTA

Examiner's Tip

Using reverse transcriptase the exact piece of DNA which codes for the production of a vital protein can be made.

Genetically modified organisms

Animals and plants can also have their DNA changed. A new gene can be added to give the organism a new property or feature.

Genetically modified soya bean plants

In the USA large quantities of soya beans are produced.

- Selective herbicides (weedkillers) could not be used in soya bean fields because the crop is also killed.
- Genetic engineers transferred a gene using a **vector** into a soya bean plant which gave resistance to selective herbicides.
- The vector was a bacterium which entered the soya bean plant, taking the useful gene with it.
- Genetically modified soya seeds are now grown all over the world.
- Farmers use selective herbicides in their soya fields and keep them weed free so that yields have improved.

Genetically modified potato plants

- A gene which allows the production of insecticide has been transferred into a new breed of potato plant.
- Aphids which feed on the sap of the plants take in the insecticide which kills many of them.
- It is not 100% effective so there are many resistant aphids in the environment.
- Ladybirds are natural predators which eat the aphids.
- It has been found that ladybird fertility has decreased, and they live half as long as normal.
- In the long term the aphid pests may increase even more, becoming a greater problem and ladybirds could even become extinct.

Ethical issues

The applications of gene technology have huge implications. People must assess the advantages against the potential dangers.

- It is possible to locate a defective gene in a fetus. Consider the responsibility of knowing this information.
- Companies now are able to change a species drastically to produce something useful to humans. Is it moral to change a species?
- If potatoes contain insecticide which kills aphids and their ladybird predators, what effect may it have on human consumers of the genetically modified potatoes?

Life is based on DNA. Different species possess DNA with different sequences of organic bases. Adding new sections to give new properties has advantages but should be handled with care. There may be consequences.

Examiner's Tip

Always qualify your view of ethics with scientific back up. It is your scientific reasoning which scores the marks.

Progress check

1 The sequence of organic bases below codes for *four* amino acids.

CTG GTG TAC AAG

a Use the key and table on pp. 58–59 to work out the amino acid sequence.

b The sequence shown mutates to:

CTG GTG TAC GAA

i What type of mutation is shown?

ii What would be the new amino acid produced as a result of the mutation?

2 a The statements below describe *two* processes which take place during protein synthesis.

i tRNA links with mRNA to bond amino acids together.

ii DNA forms mRNA in the nucleus.

Name processes i and ii.

b Name the bond which links two amino acids together.

3 The statements below describe how the human gene for insulin production was engineered into a bacterium, resulting in the production of insulin. The letters are in the wrong order. Give the letters which show the correct order.

a A plasmid was taken from a bacterium and cut with the same restriction endonuclease.

b The human gene for insulin was inserted into the plasmid.

c **Restriction endonuclease** cut the DNA and the gene was removed.

d Large numbers of the new bacteria were produced, each able to secrete human insulin.

e The gene was made to fix into the open plasmid by **ligase**.

f The plasmid **replicated** inside the bacterium.

Answers on page 93

Continuity of life

Variation

Why is meiosis so important in sexual reproduction?

When sexual reproduction takes place, the male and female produce gametes (sex cells) by the process of meiosis.

- parental cell has chromosomes in pairs (diploid)

- four daughter cells each have single chromosomes, half the number of the parental cell (haploid)

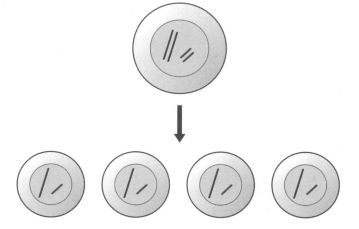

Main features of meiosis

- All cells produced by meiosis are **different** to the parental cell and to each other (a major factor in the **genetic variation** within a species!).
- Four cells are produced, each having single chromosomes.

How are genetically different cells produced during meiosis?

The key event in producing genetically different gametes takes place during the first stage of meiosis – **prophase 1**. The diagrams show the process of **crossing over** of a pair of homologous chromosomes to produce **different allele combinations**.

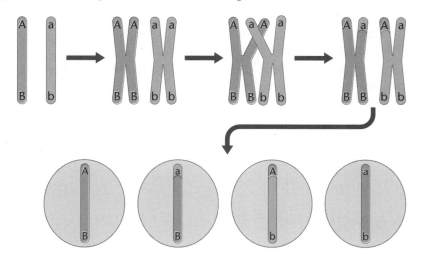

A represents an allele dominant to **a**, a recessive allele.

B represents an allele dominant to **b**, a recessive allele.

(An allele is a different expression of a gene.)

(continued next page)

What effect do cross-overs have on variation?

- Each pair of alleles along homologous chromosome pairs can be homozygous, e.g. AA, aa; or heterozygous, e.g. Aa (where A is **dominant**, and a is **recessive**).
- The chromosomes would have many more genes than merely ones shown by A, a, B, b. The previous diagram shows the consequence of only one **cross-over** or **chiasma**.
- Cross-overs or chiasmata cause a difference in the combinations of alleles along a chromosome.
- The cross-over, as shown, results in chromosomes with AB, Ab, aB and ab combinations.
- With **many cross-overs** taking place along **all 23 pairs of chromosomes**, it is not surprising that every cell produced by meiosis is **genetically different**.

Meiosis takes place by two divisions. Consider these two divisions in relation to the cross-over shown.

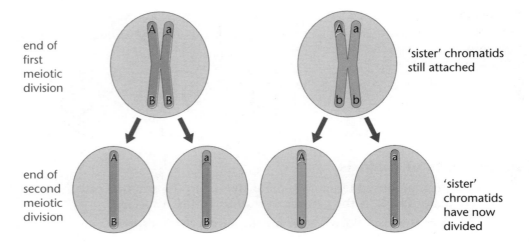

end of first meiotic division

'sister' chromatids still attached

end of second meiotic division

'sister' chromatids have now divided

- The combination of each of these chromosomes with 22 others, results in further genetic variation.
- This is the **random segregation** of chromosomes.
- Human gametes are produced by meiosis (only one homologous pair is shown in the diagram but there would be 22 other pairs).
- If each gamete is different, then the male gamete fusing with a female gamete is yet another source of variation.

Humans are given as examples of the consequences of a meiotic division. Plants and other organisms divide by **exactly the same principles**. Only the chromosome numbers and alleles differ.

Examiner's Tip

You will often be tested on your knowledge of variation. Three causes of variation to remember are: cross-overs during meiosis; the random segregation of chromosomes; and mutations, which are ultimately responsible for new features.

Energy and ecosystems

What is an ecosystem?

The study of **ecology** investigates the inter-relationships between organisms in an area and their environment. The importance of photosynthesis to all organisms of an ecosystem must be considered. The plants (producers) make carbohydrates and are the source of most energy available to the organisms of an ecosystem. Before explaining the term 'ecosystem', some important terms need to be defined.

- **Habitat** is the area where an organism lives.
- **Population** is the number of organisms of one species living in an area.
- **Community** is a number of different populations living in an area.
- **Biotic factors** are factors caused by living organisms which influence other organisms in their environment, e.g. plants being consumed by herbivores or one species predating upon another.
- **Abiotic factors** are non-living factors which influence organisms in their environment, e.g. pH of the soil or the temperature of the environment.
- **Niche** is the precise way in which an organism fits into its environment and what it does there, e.g. a fish may survive within a temperature range of 30–35°C, and a pH range of 5–8, and eat a specific type of plant. All of its specific requirements for life are its niche.
- **Competition** is where different organisms occupy a similar niche, e.g. slugs and snails living in a garden both consume lettuce leaves.

An **ecosystem** is a distinctive and stable ecological unit in an area and consists of the following features:
- different populations of organisms living and interacting together within a **community**
- all **abiotic factors** of their environment
- the **energy flow** through food chains and webs
- the **cycling of nutrients** to be reused by the community.

There may be no physical barrier between one ecosystem and the next, e.g. a desert ecosystem may exist alongside a tropical ecosystem, which has much more rainfall. Each specific ecosystem is **self-sustaining** and relies on the **cycling of nutrients** and special **adaptations of the component organisms.**

Examiner's Tip

Some organisms may move from one ecosystem to another, e.g. a dragonfly larva is part of a food web in a pond, but after reaching the maturity of adulthood it flies into a terrestrial ecosystem.

Energy flow through an ecosystem

Sunlight energy enters the ecosystem and *some* is available for photosynthesis. *Not all* light energy reaches photosynthetic tissues.

- Some light totally misses plants and may be absorbed or reflected by such items as water, rock or soil.
- Some light energy may be reflected by the waxy cuticle or even miss chloroplasts completely!
- A green plant uses **carbohydrate** as a first stage substance and goes on to make **proteins** and **lipids**.
- Plants are a rich source of nutrients, available to the herbivores which eat the plants. Some energy is not available to the herbivores for two reasons:
  1. Green plants **respire** (releasing energy).
  2. Not **all parts** of plants may be **consumed**, e.g. roots.

Food chains and webs

Each food chain always begins with an autotroph (producer), then energy is passed to a primary consumer, then secondary consumer, then tertiary consumer and so on.

Producer →   primary consumer →   secondary consumer →   tertiary consumer
               (herbivore)   (1st carnivore)   (2nd carnivore)

The following example shows four food chains linked to form a food web.

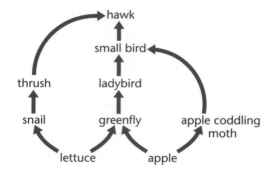

Each feeding level along a food chain can also be represented by a **trophic level**. The food chain on the next page is taken from the food web above and illustrates trophic levels.

Energy may be used by an organism in a number of different ways:

- respiration releases energy for movement or maintenance of body temperature, etc.
- production of new cells in growth and repair
- production of eggs.

Energy flow along a food chain

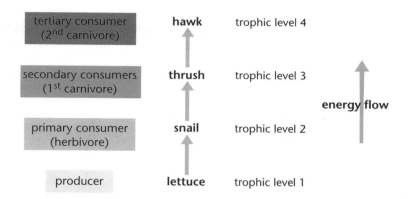

Predators and prey

- Primary consumers rely on the **producers**, so a flush of new vegetation results in an increase in the numbers of primary consumers.
- Predators which eat the primary consumers follow with a population increase.
- Each population of the ecosystem may have a **sequential effect** on other populations.
- Ultimately the ecosystem is in **dynamic equilibrium** and has limits as to how many of each population can survive, i.e. its **carrying capacity**.

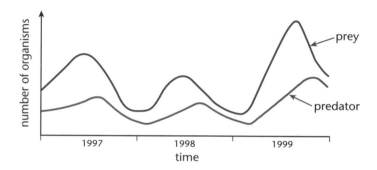

The nitrogen cycle

Nitrogen is found in every amino acid, protein, DNA and RNA. It is an essential element! Most organisms are unable to use atmospheric nitrogen directly so the nitrogen cycle is very important.

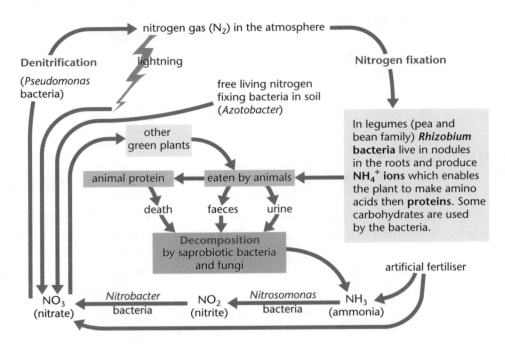

Some important points

- Nitrogen gas from the atmosphere is used by *Rhizobium* bacteria. These bacteria, living in nodules of legume plants, convert nitrogen into ammonia (NH_3), then into amine ($-NH_2$) compounds. The plants then make proteins. The bacteria gain carbohydrates from the plant.

- Dead organic material is useful to the ecosystem, but first decomposition by saprotrophs takes place; a waste product of this process is ammonia.

- Ammonia is needed by *Nitrosomonas* bacteria which produce nitrite ($-NO_2$).

- Nitrite is needed by *Nitrobacter* bacteria which make nitrate, vital for plant growth. Plants absorb large quantities of nitrates via their roots.

- Nitrogen gas is returned to the atmosphere by denitrifying bacteria such as *Azotobacter* which change the nitrate to nitrogen.

The cycle is complete!

Progress check

1 The statements below define some important terms. Choose the correct word from the list which is defined by a statement

biotic factors
population
abiotic factors
habitat
community
niche
competition

a   The number of organisms of one species living in an area.

b   The precise way in which an organism fits into its environment and what it does there, e.g. a fish may survive within a temperature range of 30–35°C, and a pH range of 5–8 and eat a specific type of plant. All of its specific requirements for life are its niche.

c   Factors caused by living organisms which influence other organisms in their environment, e.g. plants being consumed by herbivores or one species predating upon another.

d   Where different organisms occupy a similar niche, e.g. slugs and snails living in a garden both consume lettuce leaves.

e   The area where an organism lives.

f   A number of different populations living in an area.

g   Non-living factors which influence organisms in their environment, e.g. pH of the soil or the temperature of the environment.

2 What effect does acid rain have on the absorption of mineral ions by plants?

3 a   An organism has died. Explain how nitrogen gas may be returned to the atmosphere after this event.

  b   i   Name a plant which can make use of atmospheric nitrogen after it has been fixed by bacteria.

      ii   *Rhizobium* is a species of bacterium which can do this. Where, precisely, would the process of nitrogen fixation take place?

Answers on page 93

Human health and disease

Effects of lifestyle

Statistically people have a greater chance of living longer if they:

- do not smoke
- do not drink alcohol excessively
- consume a low amount of salt
- consume a low amount of saturated fat in their diet
- are not stressed most of the time
- exercise regularly.

Exercise

Exercise has a **protective effect** on the **heart** and **circulation**. Activities such as jogging, walking, swimming and cycling can build up the person's endurance.

Doing a minor amount of exercise, infrequently is ineffective. The **intensity**, **frequency** and **duration** of the exercise are all important.

Frequent exercise:

- reduces the resting heart rate
- increases the strength of contraction of the heart muscle
- increases the stroke volume of the heart (the volume of blood which is propelled during the contractions of the ventricles)
- aids mobility and suppleness of the body
- increases the rate of recovery after a strenuous activity, so that heart rate and breathing rates return to resting levels more quickly.

Recommended amount of exercise per week:

- **intensity** – should allow your heart to beat at a minimum of 60% of your maximum heart rate and increase as you become more fit
- **frequency** – around three times weekly
- **duration** – about 30–60 minutes per session.

The diagrams below show the typical effect of training on a person's heart.

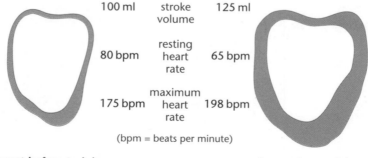

	heart before training		heart after training
stroke volume	100 ml		125 ml
resting heart rate	80 bpm		65 bpm
maximum heart rate	175 bpm		198 bpm

(bpm = beats per minute)

heart before training   heart after training

Pulse rate

- During the contraction of the ventricles (systole) blood is forced at high pressure through the arteries.
- As a result a wave of blood flow passes which causes a momentary expansion at an artery.
- The pulse is usually taken at the wrist because the expansion in an artery close to the skin surface can be detected against an underlying bone.
- It is important that a pulse is taken with a finger rather than a thumb. The thumb has a detectable pulse of its own!
- There are a number of other ideal positions around the body where the pulse can be taken e.g. temporal pulse on the side of the head.
- The number of pulses in a minute gives the pulse rate.
- Pulse rate increases as we become more active, as the body needs to achieve greater gaseous exchange.

Hypertension

- is a persistent high blood pressure exceeding 11.9 kilopascals.
- is a major factor in a range of cardiovascular diseases including strokes, coronary heart disease and atherosclerosis

Occurrence of coronary heart disease

On a worldwide basis the disease is often associated with the economic status of the country and lifestyle. A number of factors need to be taken into consideration.

- Intake of excessive carbohydrate and/or animal fat can result in the narrowing of blood vessels.
- An inactive lifestyle impairs the functioning of the cardiovascular system.
- Smoking tobacco (see p 82) also impairs the functioning of the cardiovascular system.
- Countries with economic problems lack suitable nutrient supplies to the people leading to poor cardiovascular development in the young and increased heart problems in the elderly.

Aerobic exercise

- Aerobic respiration takes place in the cells with the help of mitochondria.
- During this form of respiration a substrate such as glucose is completely oxidized to carbon dioxide and water.
- Step up routines and jogging are aerobic exercises which stimulate this type of respiration.
- Large amounts of substrate carbohydrates and fat can be metabolized.
- Long term aerobic exercise reduces the chance of developing cardiovascular problems and/or obesity.
- Aerobic exercise which releases approximately 35 000 kj in a week can reduce body fat by 1 kg!

Anaerobic respiration

- Substrates release energy without oxygen being involved.
- Less energy is released than during aerobic respiration.
- In the cells glucose forms lactate.
- Lactate results in oxygen debt.
- A sprint race is fuelled almost exclusively by anaerobic respiration.
- At the end of a sprint race the oxygen debt is repaid as the athlete breathes heavily.
- Lactate is converted to pyruvate where it enters the aerobic metabolic route.

Examiner's Tip

A combination of factors is responsible for our health. Try to remember them all!

Survival against the attack of pathogens

Many pathogenic organisms attack people. They are not all successful in causing disease. We have immunity to a disease when we are able to resist infection. The body has a range of ways to prevent the disease causing organism from becoming established.

- A tough protein called **keratin** helps skin cells to be a formidable **barrier** to prevent pathogens entering the body.
- An enzyme, **lysozyme**, destroys some microorganisms and is found in sebum, tears and saliva.
- **Hydrochloric acid** in the stomach kills some microorganisms.
- Lungs are lined with **cilia**. Microorganisms which enter the respiratory system are often trapped in mucus which is moved to the oesophagus. From here they move to the stomach where many are destroyed by hydrochloric acid or digested.
- **Blood clotting** in response to external damage prevents entry of microorganisms from the external environment.

Sometimes microorganisms invade successfully, then breed in high numbers, so we develop **symptoms**. White blood cells enable us to destroy invading microorganisms.

The role of white blood cells (leucocytes)

There are different types of **leucocyte**.

- They are all produced from **stem cells** in the **bone marrow**.
- Different stem cells follow alternative maturation procedures to produce a range of leucocytes.
- Leucocytes have the ability to recognise self chemicals and non-self.
- Only where non-self chemicals are recognised will a leucocyte respond.
- Proteins and polysaccharides are typical of the complex molecules which can trigger an immune response.

White blood cells (leucocytes) constantly check out proteins around the body. Foreign protein is identified and attack is stimulated.

Phagocytes

- Phagocytes can move to a site of infection through capillaries, tissue fluid and lymph, as well as being found in the plasma.
- They move towards pathogens which they destroy by phagocytosis (often called engulfment); this involves the surrounding of a pathogen by pseudopodia. Enzymes complete the destruction of the pathogen.

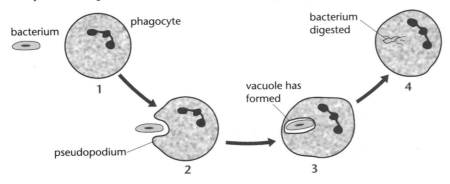

What is an antigen?

As an individual grows and develops, complex substances such as proteins and polysaccharides are used to form cellular structures.

- Leucocytes identify these substances in the body as 'self' substances. They are ignored as the leucocytes encounter them daily.
- 'Non-self substances', e.g. foreign proteins which enter the body are identified as 'non-self'.
- These are known as **antigens** and trigger an immune response.

Lymphocytes

There are two types of lymphocyte, **B-lymphocytes** and **T-lymphocytes**.

B-lymphocytes begin development and mature in the bone marrow. They produce antibodies; this is known as the **humoral response**.

T-lymphocytes work alongside phagocytes known as macrophages. A macrophage engulfs an antigen. This antigen remains on the surface of the macrophage. T-lymphocytes respond to the antigen, dividing by mitosis to form a range of different types of T-lymphocyte cells.

- **Killer T-lymphocytes** adhere to the pathogen, secrete a toxin and destroy it.
- **Helper T-lymphocytes** stimulate the production of antibodies.
- **Suppressor T-lymphocytes** are inhibitors of the T-lymphocytes and plasma cells. Just weeks after the initial infection, they shut down the immune response when it is no longer needed.
- **Memory T-lymphocytes** respond to an antigen previously experienced. They are able to destroy the same pathogen before symptoms appear.

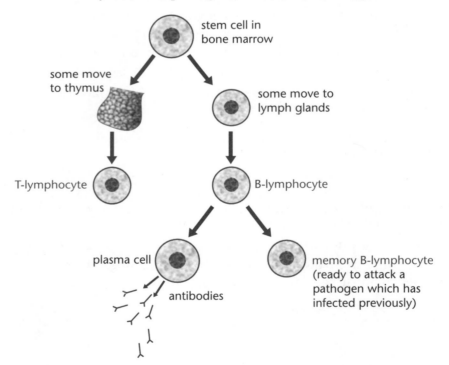

stem cell in bone marrow

some move to thymus

some move to lymph glands

T-lymphocyte

B-lymphocyte

plasma cell

antibodies

memory B-lymphocyte (ready to attack a pathogen which has infected previously)

Examiner's Tip

Don't forget the memory B-lymphocytes which can, when stimulated, lead to antibody production. When the same pathogen returns the memory B lymphocytes give protection.

The importance of diet

A balanced diet is vital to good health. The main food categories are given below.

- **Carbohydrates** include sugars and starch that supply metabolic energy. Cellulose (dietary fibre) stimulates peristalsis so that constipation is prevented.

  Source – potato and bread.

- **Proteins** supply metabolic energy and are needed in growth and repair. **All enzymes are proteins.** Very important!

  Source – meat and nuts.

- **Fats and oils** supply metabolic energy and are needed in cell membrane formation as they help to make phospholipids.

  Source – butter and cooking oil

- **Vitamins** are **organic** substances needed in minute quantities to maintain health, e.g. vitamin A. This is essential to make the pigment in the rods of the retina. Vitamin D helps develop healthy bones.

  Source – (vitamin A) butter and carrots, (vitamin D) oily fish and eggs.

- **Minerals** are inorganic ions needed for a number of important roles in the body e.g. iron. This is essential for the production of haemoglobin and so is vital for oxygen transport.

  Source (iron) – red meat, spinach

- **Water** makes over 50% of content of blood plasma. It is needed for many functions including as a solvent and cooling the body down.

- **Fibre** stimulates peristalsis so that the intestines function correctly.

What effect does the amount of food eaten have on health?

- A lack of any one dietary constituent may result in a deficiency disease.
- A lack of vitamin A leads to poor sight in dim light conditions.
- A lack of vitamin D results in the malformation of bone joints (rickets.)
- A lack of protein leads to kwashiorkor.
- Very low quantities of food results in wasting.
- Too much carbohydrate and fat results in obesity and associated cardiovascular problems.

A balanced diet is vital!

Essential amino acids

Amino acids bond to form proteins. **Essential amino acids** must be supplied in the diet and cannot be made in the body. A person who eats foods with all the essential amino acids is able to make the others. Infants need 10 essential amino acids but adults need just 8. Similarly, essential fatty acids cannot be made and must be directly consumed. They can be used as an energy source.

There are 20 different amino acids used to make proteins.

Daily energy requirement

Energy is released from food during respiration. Carbohydrates, proteins, fats and oils supply the energy which is measured in **kilojoules (kJ)**.

What are the energy needs of different people?

Energy needs are determined by age, gender, and activity. Additionally, if a woman is pregnant or lactating, extra food is needed. The table below shows typical daily energy requirements.

Person	Energy used in one day (kilojoules)			
baby (0–3 months)	2 400			
infant (1 year)	4 300			
child (8 years)	8 900			
teenager (15 years)	Male	12 600	Female	9 600
adult (office work)	Male	11 600	Female	9 500
adult (heavy work)	Male	16 600	Female	12 600
pregnant woman	10 500			
lactating mother	11 400			

When a person is sleeping their respiratory rate is at a minimum, so the amount of energy released from food is also at a minimum. Exercise is important for health. It can prevent excessive weight increase since more kilojoules of energy are released by increased respiratory activity. If the energy component and the other components of the diet are less than the recommended daily values malnutrition takes place. This resembles multiple deficiency diseases. Muscle wastage follows and the individual is in great danger.

Examiner's Tip

Try to learn a range of examples for all the food components. Don't forget that the diet is just one influence on health. There are others, including your level of physical exercise.

A combination of factors is responsible for our health!

Saturated fat and coronary heart disease

- An example of part of the diet which should be eaten in small quantities is **saturated fat**.
- Saturated fats are found in large quantities in animal tissues, e.g. fatty pork chops.
- The way that the food is cooked can also result in health problems. Frying food in animal fat adds to the danger!

What is atherosclerosis?

This is a major health problem caused by eating saturated fats. This circulatory disease may develop as follows:

- yellow fatty streaks develop under the lining of the **endothelium** on the inside of an artery
- the streaks develop into a fatty lump called an **atheroma**
- the atheroma is made from **cholesterol** (taken up in the diet as well as being made in the liver)

- dense **fibrous tissue** develops as the atheroma grows
- the endothelial lining can split, allowing blood to contact the fibrous atheroma
- the damage may lead to a blood clot and an artery can be blocked.

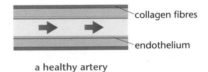

collagen fibres

endothelium

a healthy artery

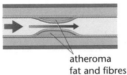

atheroma
fat and fibres

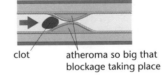

clot   atheroma so big that blockage taking place

Increasing constriction of an artery caused by **atherosclerosis** and **blood clots** reduces blood flow and increases blood pressure. If the artery wall is considerably weakened then a bulge in the side appears, just like a weakened inner tube on a cycle tyre. There is a danger of bursting and the structure is known as an **aneurysm**.

It is possible for a blood clot formed at an atheroma to break away from its original position. It may completely block a smaller vessel, this is known as an **embolism**.

If the artery which supplies the heart (coronary artery) is partially blocked, then there is a reduction in oxygen and nutrient supply to the heart itself. This causes **angina**, the main symptom being sharp chest pains. If total blockage occurs then **myocardial infarction** (heart attack) takes place.

Examiner's Tip

You may be given a diagram showing a blockage caused by atheroma. Be ready to state increase in blood pressure then go on to predict other *sequential* effects. More able students give more detail.

What are the dangers of smoking tobacco?

Each person has another choice to make, to smoke or not to smoke. The government health warning on every cigarette packet informs of health dangers but many young people go ahead and ignore the information.

Effects of tobacco smoking

- **Nicotine** is the active component in tobacco which addicts people to the habit.

- Tars coat the alveoli which slows down exchange of carbon dioxide and oxygen. If less oxygen is absorbed then the smoker will be less active than their true potential.

- Cilia lining bronchial tubes are coated then destroyed, this reduces the efficiency in getting rid of pollutants which enter the lungs. These pollutants include the cigarette chemicals themselves.

- **Carbon monoxide** from the cigarette gases combines with haemoglobin of red blood cells rather than oxygen. This reduces oxygen transport and the smoker becomes less active than their potential. Ultimately it may lead to heart disease.

- The **bronchi** and **bronchioles** become inflamed, a condition known as **bronchitis**. This causes irritating fluid in the lungs, coughing and increased risk of heart disease. A number of bronchitis sufferers die each year.

- The walls of the alveoli break down reducing the surface area for gaseous exchange. Less oxygen can be absorbed by the lungs leaving the **emphysema** sufferer extremely breathless. They increase their breathing rate to compensate but still cannot take in enough oxygen for a healthy life. A chronic emphysema sufferer needs an oxygen cylinder to prolong their life. Death is a regular conclusion, especially when combined with other symptoms.

- Blood vessel elasticity is reduced so that serious damage may occur. Ultimately a heart attack can follow.

- The **carcinogens** (cancer-causing chemicals) in the tobacco can result in **lung cancer**. **Malignant growths** in the lungs develop uncontrollably and cancers may spread to other parts of the body. Death often follows. Smokers have a greater risk of developing other cancers than non-smokers, e.g. more smokers develop cervical cancer.

The role of statistics

The government health warning on cigarette packets informs people of the risks of smoking. The WHO (World Health Authority), governments and local authorities have collected statistics on many diseases over the years. These are used in education packs and posters to warn of risk factors. People can take precautions and use the information to avoid health dangers. Where education is not successful then related diseases follow. This acts as a drain on the National Health Service. Many operations which would have been unnecessary are performed to save people's lives, e.g. where coronary blood vessels are dangerously diseased and a by-pass operation is the answer.

The ideal situation is that education is successful, but realistically the aim is to balance prevention and cure.

Examiner's Tip

Remember to give all of the details about the effects of tobacco smoking, when asked. Reduced gaseous exchange caused by emphysema is commonly tested.

What is a disease?

It is a **disorder** of a tissue, organ or system of an organism. As a result of the disorder, **symptoms** are evident. Normal bodily processes may be disrupted, e.g. efficient oxygen transport is impeded by the malarial parasite, *Plasmodium*.

Different types of disease

Infectious disease by pathogens.

- Pathogens attack an organism.
- Many pathogens are spread by a **vector** which carries it from one organism to another without itself being affected by the disease.

Genetic diseases

- These can be passed from parent to offspring.
- Also known as **congenital diseases**, they include haemophilia and cystic fibrosis.

Dietary related diseases

- These are caused by the foods we eat: too much or too little food may cause disorders.

Environmentally caused diseases.

- Some aspects of the environment disrupt bodily processes, e.g. as a result of nuclear radiation leakage, cancer may develop.

Auto-immune disease

- The body in some way attacks its own cells so that processes fail to function effectively, e.g. motor neurone disease This is a degenerative disease.

How are infectious diseases transmitted?

- By direct contact, e.g. sexual intercourse enables the transmission of syphilis bacteria; a person's foot which touches a damp floor at the swimming baths can transfer the athlete's foot fungus.
- By droplet infection. A sneeze propels tiny droplets of nasal mucus carrying viruses such as those causing influenza.
- Via a vector, e.g. if a person with typhoid bacteria in the gut handles food the bacteria can be passed to a susceptible person.
- Via food or water, e.g. chicken meat kept in warm conditions encourages the reproduction of *Salmonella* bacteria which are transferred to the human consumer, who has food poisoning as a result.
- Via blood transfusion, as a result of receiving blood a person can contract a number of infectious diseases e.g. AIDS.

Infectious disease

The infectious diseases in an area may be classified by using the following terms:

(a) endemic, which means that a disease or its vector is invariably found in an area.

(b) epidemic, which means that there is an outbreak of a disease attacking many people in an area.

(c) pandemic, which means that a there is an outbreak of a disease over a very large area, e.g. the size of a continent.

Disease file – cholera

Cause of disease

Vibrio cholerae (bacteria).

Transmission of microorganism

Contaminated water spreads the bacteria. Poor sanitary behaviour of people who are carriers and those who suffer from the disease is responsible. Faeces enter rivers which may be used for bathing, drinking, or irrigation. The bacteria survive outside the human body for around 24 hours.

Outline of the course of disease and symptoms

The bacteria reach the intestines where they breed. They secrete a toxin which stimulates adenyl cyclase in epithelial cells. This enzyme causes much fluid to be secreted into the intestine, giving severe diarrhoea. Death is a regular consequence due to dehydration but some people do recover.

Prevention

Education about cleanliness and sewage treatment. Good sanitation is vital. Suitable treatment of water to be consumed by people, e.g. chlorination which kills the bacteria. Use of disinfectant also kills the bacteria. Early identification of an outbreak followed by control.

Cure

Tetracycline antibiotics kill bacteria in the bowel.

Immunization is not very effective. It will help some individuals but not stop them from being carriers, so epidemics are still likely.

Examiner's Tip

Most exam candidates recall that pathogens are responsible for disease. However, there are more causes of disease! If a question asks for different types of disease then giving a range of pathogens will not score many marks. Give genetic diseases, etc.

Disease file – tuberculosis

Cause of disease

Mycobacterium tuberculosis (bacterium).

Transmission of microorganism

Coughs and sneezes of sufferers spread tiny droplets of moisture containing the pathogenic bacteria. People then inhale these droplets and may contract the disease.

Outline of the course of the disease and symptoms

The initial attack takes place in the lungs. The alveoli surfaces and capillaries are vulnerable and lesions occur. Some epithelial tissues begin to grow in number but these cannot carry out gaseous exchange. Inflammation occurs which stimulates painful coughing. Intense coughing takes place which can cause bleeding. There is much weight loss. Weak groups of people, like the elderly, or someone underweight are more prone to the disease.

Prevention

Mass screening using X-rays can identify 'shadows' in those people with scar tissue in the lungs.

Sputum testing identifies the presence of the bacteria in sufferers.

Sufferers can be treated with antibiotics. Once cured they cannot pass on the pathogen so an epidemic may be prevented.

Skin testing is used. Antigens from dead *Mycobacteria* are injected just beneath the skin. If a person has been previously exposed to the organism then the skin swells which shows that they already have resistance, i.e. they have antibodies already. Anyone whose skin does not swell up is given the **BCG vaccination**. This contains attenuated *Mycobacterium bovis* to stimulate the production of antibodies against both *M. bovis* and *M tuberculosis*.

Cure

Use of antibiotics such as streptomycin.

Mycobacterium bovis causes tuberculosis in cattle. It can be passed to humans via milk. It causes an intestinal complaint in humans. It is important that cows are kept free of *M. bovis* by antibiotics.

The BCG vaccination is the injection of a weakened form of this microbe. This vaccination stimulates antibodies which are effective against both *M. tuberculosis* and *M.bovis*.

Combinations of these tests are used in different countries. Where there are outbreaks of the disease the systems are activated.

Disease file – malaria

Cause of disease

There are many variants of the malarial parasite, *Plasmodium* (protozoa).

Transmission of the microorganism

- The vector which carries the *Plasmodium* is a female *Anopheles* mosquito.
- The mosquito feeds on a mammal which may be suffering from malaria.
- It does this at night by inserting its 'syringe-like' stylet into a blood vessel beneath the skin.
- The mosquito feeds on blood and digests the red blood cells which releases the malarial parasites.
- These burrow into the insect's stomach wall where they breed then move to the salivary glands.
- Next time the mosquito feeds it secretes saliva to prevent clotting of the blood.
- This secretion introduces the parasites into the person's blood, who is likely to contract the disease.

Outline of the course of the disease and symptoms

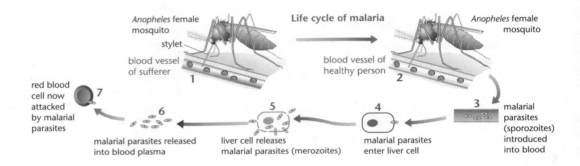

Anopheles female mosquito
stylet
blood vessel of sufferer
1

Life cycle of malaria

Anopheles female mosquito
blood vessel of healthy person
2

3 malarial parasites (sporozoites) introduced into blood

4 malarial parasites enter liver cell

5 liver cell releases malarial parasites (merozoites)

6 malarial parasites released into blood plasma

7 red blood cell now attacked by malarial parasites

- After entry into the blood **sporozoites** invade the liver releasing many **merozoites**.
- Each merozoite infects a red blood cell producing even more merozoites.
- Millions of these parasites are released into the blood causing a fever.
- The sufferer develops a range of symptoms including pains, exhaustion, aching, feeling cold, sweating and fever.
- The increased body temperature attracts mosquitoes even more, so a person with malaria acts as a reservoir for parasites.

Prevention

- The most effective methods of prevention are those which destroy the vector.
- Spraying **insecticide** onto lake surfaces kills mosquito larvae.
- Oil poured on lake surfaces prevents air entering the breathing tubes of the mosquito larvae, so they die.
- Fish can be introduced into lakes as predators to eat the larvae. This is an example of **biological control**.
- Sometimes ponds are **drained** to remove the mosquitoes' breeding area. People in areas where malaria is endemic cover up all waste tin cans and plastic containers. If these were to fill up with rain water then the mosquitoes have another habitat to breed in.
- The bacterium, Bacillis thuringiensis is used to destroy mosquitoes.
- Mosquito nets exclude mosquitoes from buildings and are even used over beds.
- **Electronic insect killer** techniques can be used which attract the mosquito via ultraviolet light then kill them by application of voltage.
- Drugs are used so that even if a person is bitten by a mosquito any *Plasmodia* entering the blood fail to develop further.

Cure

It is necessary to isolate and treat the sufferer. This also reduces the spread of the disease. Drugs are used to kill the parasites in the blood and reduce the symptoms. People are constantly attempting to find different ways of preventing this killer disease.

Global warming is beginning to have an effect on the distribution of the disease. New areas suitable as habitats for the *Anopheles* mosquito are appearing because of global warming.

Disease file – AIDS (Acquired Immune Deficiency Syndrome)

Cause of disease

HIV (human immune deficiency virus). It is a retrovirus, which is able to make DNA from its own core of RNA.

Transmission of microorganism

This takes place by the exchange of body fluids, transfusion of contaminated blood, or via syringe needle 'sharing' in drug practices.

Outline of the course of the disease and symptoms

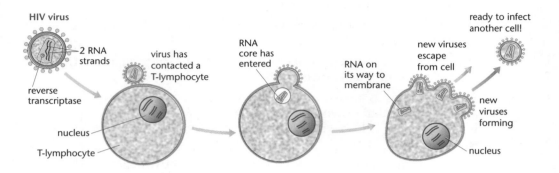

Destruction of T-lymphocyte cells:

- The HIV protein coat attaches to protein in the plasma membrane of a T-lymphocyte.
- The virus protein coat fuses with the cell membrane releasing RNA and reverse transcriptase into the cell.
- This enzyme causes the cell to produce DNA from the viral RNA.
- This DNA enters the nucleus of the T-lymphocyte and is incorporated into the host cell chromosomes.
- The gene representing the HIV virus is permanently in the nucleus from now on, and can be dormant for years but become activated by an infection.
- Viral protein and viral RNA are made as a result of the infection.
- Many RNA viral cores now leave the cell, and protein coats are assembled from degenerating plasma membranes.
- Other T-lymphocytes are attacked. Cells of the lymph nodes and spleen are also destroyed.
- Viruses appear in the blood, tears, saliva, semen and vaginal fluids. The immune system becomes so weak that many diseases can now successfully invade the weakened body.

Prevention

- Screening of blood before transfusions.
- Use of condoms and remaining with one partner.
- No use of contaminated needles.

Examiner's Tip

The OCR specification includes all of the diseases in this chapter. In your examination take care to match the facts to the correct disease. Check out this scenario; the question is about cholera and you give the facts for TB. In a major question this could lose around 10 marks. Learn all of the details carefully!

Progress check

1 The diagram below shows the sequence which takes place as B-lymphocytes respond to an antigen.

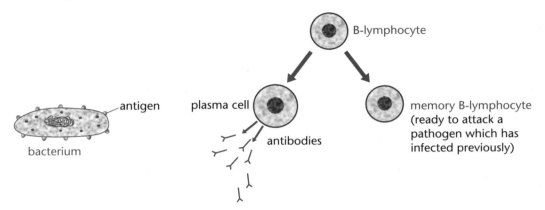

a Describe the sequence of events which results in the destruction of the bacterium.

b Explain how a person can become immune to a pathogenic disease after contracting it once only.

2 The diagram below shows a phagocyte about to destroy a bacterium.

Describe what happened immediately:

a before this stage

b after this stage.

3 Explain how antibodies destroy microbes by using:

a precipitation

b lysis.

4 The following statements give examples of different types of disease.

a The body produces antibodies against the molecules in the gut which aid the absorption of vitamin B_{12}.

b People who have cystic fibrosis have two alleles which result in the disease.

c *Anopheles* mosquitoes pass on the *Plasmodium* organisms to a person who then contracts malaria.

d Leakage of radiation at the nuclear power station resulted in cancer.

Link each statement with the correct disease from the list below.

Genetic disease 1
Dietary related disease 2
Environmentally caused disease 3
Auto-immune disease 4
Infectious disease caused by pathogen 5

(continued next page)

5 *Mycobacterium bovis* causes tuberculosis in cattle. It can be passed to humans and causes an intestinal complaint. It is important that cows are kept free of the *M. bovis* by antibiotics.

The BCG vaccination is the injection of a weakened form of this microbe. This vaccination stimulates antibodies which are effective against both *M. tuberculosis* and *M.bovis*.

Use the information above to answer the questions below

a   Why is it important
   i   to give antibiotics to cows?
   ii   to vaccinate people with a weakened form of *Mycobacterium bovis*?

b Suggest how the *Mycobacterium bovis* can be passed to humans.

6 Malaria is very common in African countries. How can transmission of the disease be prevented?

Answer on page 94

Progress check answers

Biological molecules

1 a

peptide bond

+ H₂O

    b i   hydrolysis
        ii water

2 A 3, B 4, C 2, D 2, E 1

3 a i   fatty acid (tails)
       ii they repel water
   b it has an affinity for water

4 Benedict's test is carried out first. If negative, hydrolyse by heating with dilute hydrochloric acid. A second Benedict's test is carried out. A non-reducing sugar would show brick red. Hydrolysis breaks the glycosidic bonds which release the non-reducing sugar unit.

Cells

1 c Ribosomes are found along the rough endoplasmic reticulum.
   d Aerobic respiration takes place in the mitochondria.
   e mRNA is made in the nucleolus.

2 A: E, B: P, C: P, D: E

3 a Has internal membranes called cristae
   b Membrane enclosing chemicals (normally)
   c Membrane lined with ribosomes (look like dots)

Enzymes

1 a Y, because the reaction has a lower activation energy

   b lower

   c concentration of substrate molecules, concentration of enzyme molecules, temperature, pH

2 a Molecules of similar shape to substrate are able to bind to the active site, do not react within the active site, leave after a time without any product forming. Enzyme reaction is reduced because while the inhibitor is in the active site, no substrate can enter, substrate molecules compete for the active site so the rate of reaction decreases. The higher the proportion of competitive inhibitor the slower the rate of reaction.

   b Non-competitive inhibitors, molecules which bind to some part of an enzyme other than the active site, have a different shape to the normal substrate; they change the shape of the active site which no longer allows binding of the substrate. Some substrate molecules may reach the active site before the non-competitive inhibitor. The rate of reaction is reduced.

3 a attach to a resin or an alginate

   b i Enzymes are stuck to resin or equivalent so the product can easily be removed, leaving the enzyme adhering to apparatus.

      ii No need to stop harvesting the product because the enzymes are not free to contaminate product. Pure product continuously produced.

4 CADB

Exchange

1 a Molecule X enters the receptor molecule; this opens the channel protein, Na^+ ions can pass through the opened space.

   b Release the energy needed for the process.

2 a ψ (cell) $= \psi_s + \psi_p$

   b i cell B

      ii osmosis

      iii selectively permeable

3 a The substance contacts the cell surface membrane which indents. The substance is surrounded by the membrane, forming a vacuole. Each vacuole contains the substance and an outer membrane which has detached from the cell surface membrane.

   b Vesicle is a membrane containing a substance; vesicle membrane merges with the cell surface membrane; substance expelled from the cell.

Transport

1 a   BCEF

b   myogenic

2 a   i   Oxygen moves off the red blood cell, due to carbon dioxide at the muscle. Some oxygen passes into the cell, myoglobin has a greater affinity for oxygen, much oxygen binds to myoglobin.

ii   moves it to the right and down

b   fetal haemoglobin has a greater affinity for oxygen than adult, so that oxygen will move from adult blood to the fetus where it is needed.

The genetic code

1 a   aspartic acid and histidine, methionine, phenylalanine

b   i   inversion (a point mutation)
ii   leucine

2 a   process A is translation; process B is transcription

b   peptide

3 CABEFD

Energy and ecosystems

1 a   population

b   niche

c   biotic factors

d   competition

e   habitat

f   community

g   abiotic factors

2 Fewer minerals are absorbed. This is because some ions are more easily leached, e.g. Ca^{2+} ions. PO_4^- ions become bound to clay particles and are unavailable to plants.

3 a   Decomposers decay the body, ammonia is released. *Nitrosomonas* bacteria use ammonia to produce nitrite ($-NO_2$). Nitrite is used by *Nitrobacter* bacteria which make nitrate. Denitrifying bacteria change the nitrate to nitrogen.

b   i   legume (including peas and beans)
ii   in nodules found on the roots of legumes

Human health and disease

1 a Antigens on the surface membrane of the bacterium stimulate the B-lymphocyte; each B-lymphocyte divides to form a plasma cell and memory B-lymphocyte; plasma cell secretes antibodies; antibodies bind to antigen. Various ways of destruction, e.g. lysis.

b Memory B-lymphocytes remain in body, to be used any time against the same pathogen.

2 a The phagocyte produces pseudopodia which engulf the microbe by endocytosis, forming a vacuole.

b Digestive enzymes are secreted into the vacuole and the microbe is destroyed.

3 a Precipitation links many antigens together which enables the phagocytes to engulf them.

b The cell membrane breaks open, killing the cell.

4 a 4
b 1
c 3
d 5

5 a i To destroy the *M. bovis* bacteria which would cause intestinal problems.

ii *M. bovis* stimulates antibody production, these antibodies are effective against the human form of TB, caused by *M. tuberculosis*.

b Via milk, via meat.

6 Spray insecticide onto lake surfaces to kill mosquito larvae.

Pour oil onto lake surfaces to prevent air entering the breathing tubes of the mosquito larvae, so they die.

Introduce fish into lakes as predators to eat the larvae (biological control). Drain ponds to remove the mosquitoes' breeding area.

Use the bacterium, *Bacillis thuringiensis* to destroy mosquitoes.

Use mosquito nets to exclude mosquitoes from buildings and beds.

Use drugs so that even if *Plasmodia* enter the blood they fail to develop further.

Isolate and treat sufferers to reduce the spread of the disease.

Index